THE
PHYSICS OF
SAILING
EXPLAINED

By the same author

Seven Ideas that Shook the Universe,
by N. Spielberg and B. D. Anderson
(John Wiley & Sons, Inc.)

THE
PHYSICS OF
SAILING
EXPLAINED

Bryon D. Anderson

ADLARD COLES NAUTICAL
London

Published by Adlard Coles Nautical
an imprint of A & C Black Publishers Ltd
37 Soho Square, London W1D 3QZ
www.adlardcoles.com

ISBN 0-7136-6886-5

A CIP catalogue record for this book is available from the British Library.

Printed and bound in the United States of America.

Note: while all reasonable care has been taken in the publication of this
book, the publisher takes no responsibility for the use of the methods or
products described in the book.

Acknowledgements

I would like to thank a number of people who helped me to understand how sailboats sail, talked with me about the material included here, or read the manuscript and made helpful suggestions. These people include David Allender, David Foster, Will Hubin, Alan Reichert and Philip Smith. I would especially like thank my son, James Anderson, and Will Hubin for help with preparing the figures, and Jim Lindow who first introduced me to both sailing and some of the physics involved 35 years ago. I wish to thank Adam Cort and Janine Simon at Sheridan House for the excellent editing of the manuscript. Finally, I would like to thank my wife, Joan, for her help, encouragement and presence. She is the best mate this sailor could have.

BDA February 2003.

Contents

Contents

Introduction

Although I confess to being a physicist, this book is not intended primarily for scientists and mathematicians. I believe this book will provide the answers to many of the questions that sailing enthusiasts in general wonder about, whether they are technically oriented or not. For example, why do sailors use a "full" sail like a spinnaker for downwind sailing, but not for upwind sailing? Why are some keels narrow and deep while others are long and shallow? Why do designers put "wings" on keels? What limits the speed of sailboats? Is it important to have a highly polished hull? Why do you have to trim your sails in tighter for upwind sailing? What determines the shapes of sails and of hulls? How do sails work? How do keels work? We will try to answer these and other common questions that sailors have as simply, but as fully, as possible.

The basic requirement for enjoying this book is to have an interest in sailing and in understanding the fundamental principles of physics that make sailing work. We will try to understand what is happening with the hull, the keel and the sails as they interact with the water and wind. We will also discuss the simple physics behind local and global weather, and tide patterns. The goal is to understand the physical mechanisms involved, using only a modest amount of math. The math used, when necessary, will be at the high-school algebra level, with a little geometry and trigonometry involved, as needed. Derivations of a few of the most important equations are presented, but are placed in optional "boxes," that the reader can skip without losing any of the understanding of the physics. In fact, in many ways, this book represents the kind of book I looked for when I first became interested in sailing. The object is to figure out what is "really going on" as a sailboat passes through the water. It is not intended to enable the reader to design sailboats or sails for himself, but to provide a clear understanding of how a sailboat works and why designs are generally the way they are. I believe, as most scientists do, that the basic principles of science, including those for sailing, can be presented and understood without requiring all of the detailed mathematics and engineering analyses that the expert must know in order to actually "do" the science.

Hopefully, this will be interesting for the reader.

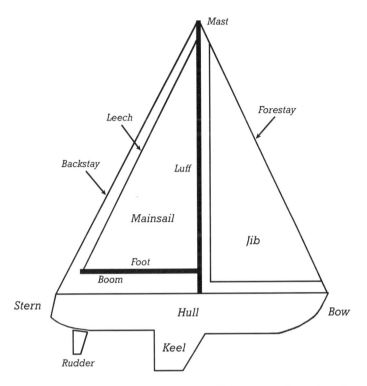

Fig. I.1 Basic sailboat terminology. This simple line drawing represents a sloop, the most common type of sailboat, with one mast, a jib (the foresail), and a mainsail.

It always helps to understand. It makes it more fun to watch the latest developments in sailboat design knowing what the basic principles are that underlie them. It also helps as you think about what you might want in a sailboat for recreational use, whether it is for club racing, cruising or just daysailing.

We will start, not with the sails, but with the hull, since it is the hull that determines the maximum speed that a sailboat can achieve, its ability to accelerate and the speed available to it in low-wind conditions. As we will see, in most cases the maximum speed that a boat can obtain is directly determined by its length. This limit comes from some simple and interesting physical properties of surface water waves. These properties lead to other interesting phenomena, and we can take a little time to discuss these as well. After that we will discuss the evolution of the shapes of hulls and what kind of resistance a hull encounters trying to move through water. This involves understanding how the friction that a boat experiences as it moves through water is fundamentally different from that of two surfaces sliding over each other. It will also address the importance of the creation of turbulence in water and air flow.

Next we will discuss the physics of keels. Keels are needed to prevent side-slipping of a sailboat and to counteract the sideways force of the wind on the sails that tends to tip the boat over. Unfortunately, keels also create additional resistance to the movement of the boat through the water, and they often are deep and limit the ability of a sailboat to move in shallow water. Therefore, the design of keels always requires some kind of balance between the necessary actions of the keel and its negative properties. We will see what kinds of solutions people have come up with for finding this balance and what principles really determine these solutions. In discussing keels, we will also need to spend a little time discussing the basic physics of wings, which will in turn help us when we discuss the physics of sails. Until about 1970, keels on sailboats were usually long and fairly deep since it was believed that this was necessary to prevent sideslipping. However, with an understanding of how "lift" can be generated from a keel much like that generated by an airplane wing, designers began to recognize that much smaller keels could not only be quite satisfactory, but that if designed properly, they offered significantly less resistance when moving through the water. We will discuss these designs.

Sails provide the power that moves a sailboat. Sails vary in shape from fairly square to very tall and narrow. We want to understand why these different shapes are used, and when they should be used. Again, everything in sailboat design is a compromise, and we want to try to understand what the competing requirements are for the design of the optimum sail for varying conditions and boats. As is generally known, a large, broad, square-shaped sail is best for straight downwind sailing, and a tall narrow sail is more efficient for sailing close to the wind direction. Again, the discussion concerning keel design will serve as a good starting point for understanding sail design since it includes an understanding of wing design, lift and vortex generation. We will try to understand these considerations as fully as possible, without getting bogged down in a lot of math or technical design considerations. After that comes a brief discussion of sail trim, i.e., how to orient and shape a sail for different wind angles and strength in the light of the physics of how sails work.

Finally, we will spend some time discussing both local and global weather, and the wind and tidal patterns of the earth. It turns out that the wind patterns are largely determined by the heating of the earth by the sun and by the fact that the earth is spinning once per day. The tidal patterns are due to the gravitational pull of the moon and sun, and the spinning of the earth. Of course, the actual patterns of winds and tides deviate from the simple predictions in detail, but it is amazing that simple models can explain the major properties of these fairly complex phenomena. For example, using simple models, we can understand the existence of the trade winds, the doldrums, the Gulf Stream and the general wind directions over all the earth.

I hope that the discussions here will enable more sailors to really understand what is going on with a sailboat moving through water, propelled by the wind and, in so doing, improve both their sailing ability and enjoyment of the sport.

1

Hulls

The hull is the main body of the boat. It is where boating begins. In fact, it is no exaggeration to say that it is the hull that makes any boat, including a sailboat, a boat. More importantly, for sailboats it is the hull that determines a number of basic performance characteristics like acceleration and maximum speed. For example, it turns out that for any boat or ship with a "displacement" hull, the maximum speed is fundamentally determined by its length. Most sailboats are displacement boats, i.e., they move *through* the water, displacing or pushing the water out of the way as they do so, and not on top of it. Fast powerboats can ride on top of the water, much like a skipping stone, thanks to a phenomenon called "planing," with the result that such boats are able to reduce water resistance dramatically and move much faster than any displacement boat. But for the most part, sailboats, with the exception of small high-powered dinghies like 470s or the latest generation of offshore racers like Volvo 60s, are unable to achieve this kind of performance for any length of time, and their top speed is limited by the pattern of waves set up as they move through the water.

Beyond that, hull *shape* determines the kind of resistance that a sailboat experiences as it moves through the water and therefore how fast it can accelerate and move in low winds. This resistance has two major components: shape resistance and surface resistance, the latter of which includes the total wetted surface of the hull plus its keel. Thanks to both kinds of resistance, as a boat moves through water it will produce turbulence in the water, both along and behind the boat. It requires energy to make this turbulence, energy that must come from the sail power. Therefore, this turbulence retards forward motion.

Finally, the shape of the hull and attached keel determines the stability of the boat, an element that is crucial to a boat's performance on many angles of sail. Let us discuss each of these aspects in turn.

1.1 Hull Speed

As everyone knows, when a boat moves through the water it generates waves. As the boat first begins to move, rather small waves are produced at the bow, with a pattern of these small waves moving back along the side of the boat. However, as the boat moves faster, the wave generated at the bow begins to have a longer and longer length, and it takes fewer and fewer waves to reach to the stern, until finally there is just one wave along the side of the boat. This wave has a crest or peak at the bow made by the bow as it pushes into the water, a trough along the center of the boat, and another crest at the stern of the boat.

Note that the length of this wave, or the "wave-length," is defined as the distance from one crest to the next; in this case from the crest at the bow to the crest at the stern. At this point, if the boat moves any faster, the wave will become even longer, and the stern will begin to fall into the trough so that the boat will be angled upward and begin to seriously plough through the water. The resistance to the forward motion then increases dramatically, and unless there is enough power available to enable the boat to jump up on top of the bow wave and start to plane, the speed of the boat reaches a natural maximum.

This progression of the wavelength with speed is shown in Figure 1.1 and occurs with all boats unable to achieve planing, in other words, displacement

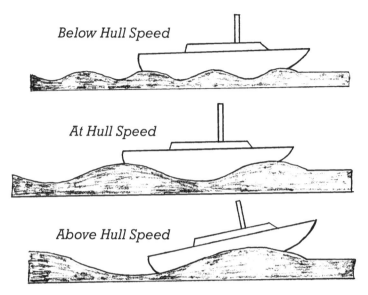

Below Hull Speed

At Hull Speed

Above Hull Speed

Figure 1.1 Bow Wave and Boat Speed. "Hull Speed" occurs when there is just one wave along the side of the boat, with a crest at the bow and the next crest at the stern of the boat.

boats like most sailboats, commercial fishing boats, naval vessels, freighters, oil tankers and cruise ships.

The relationship between the speed of the boat and the length of the wave generated is well known. It arises because surface water waves are "dispersive," i.e., their speed depends on their wavelength. The speed of the boat will be limited to the speed of the wave that has a wavelength equal to the length along the waterline of the boat. This "hull speed" effectively limits the speed of most sailboats to less than 10 knots and of most naval vessels to less than 30 knots.

With just a little algebra and some basic physics, we can derive the relationship between the speed and wavelength of a water wave. This derivation is presented in the box below. As noted in the introduction, the reader may skip this derivation without losing any understanding of the basic physics involved. However, for those who would like to see a derivation of the so-called "hull speed formula," we present it here.

Derivation of Hull Speed Formula

In general, a wave can be described by either a sine or cosine function. Let us choose the sine function so that the amplitude of the wave is zero at the origin.

$$y = A \sin (2\pi / \lambda) x ,$$

where y represents the height of the wave at horizontal position x, and A is the maximum height or "amplitude" of the wave above the normal surface of the water. The distance from one crest to the next crest is the wavelength, λ, of the wave. Such a wave is shown schematically in Figure 1.2.

Now, near the origin, where x is small, $\sin (2\pi / \lambda)$ is approximately equal to just $(2\pi / \lambda)$, i.e.,

$$\sin (2\pi / \lambda) x \approx (2\pi / \lambda) x ,$$

so that

$$y = A (2\pi / \lambda) x .$$

The ratio of y to x is then

$$y / x = A (2 \pi / \lambda).$$

Let us save this result for a little while and stop to discuss the general motion of water at the surface as a wave passes by.

Motion of Surface Particle on Water Wave

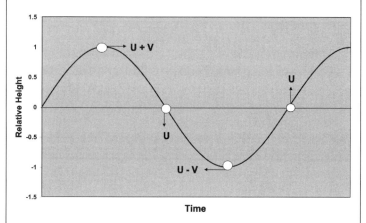

Fig. 1.2 Diagram showing motion of a particle on the surface of a water wave. The speed of the wave through the water is V; the speed of a surface particle in its circular motion as the wave passes is U. The net speed is the sum of these two speeds.

To begin with, it's important to note that the water in a surface water wave does not just move up and down as the wave passes. It also goes somewhat forward on the crest and then back again in the trough. If, for example, you place a cork in the water and watch it carefully as a wave comes by, you will see the cork move around in a circle. At the crest, the movement of the cork is forward, and in the trough it is backward, relative to the motion of the wave. (Actually, the cork will move a little more forward at the top than it moves backward at the bottom, so that there is a small net movement forward, and this effect increases with the size of the wave. But for our purpose here, we can approximate the motion as a circle.) Furthermore, if you watch the cork carefully, you will see that its speed as it moves around on the circle is constant.

This motion on the wave is indicated in Figure 1.2. Let the (constant) speed of the cork on the circle be u, and the speed of the advancing wave be v. At $y = 0$, the normal surface of the water, the speed of the cork on its circle is u and the direction is vertical, as indicated in Figure 1.2. Using the ratio of the horizontal to vertical displacements of the wave near the origin obtained above, we can relate the speed u to the speed of the moving wave, v. The ratio of the vertical to horizontal speeds is u/v and this will be the same as the ratio of y to x at the origin for the wave as obtained above. Hence we have

$$u / v \ = \ y / x \ = \ A \, (\, 2 \, \pi / \lambda \,) . \qquad (1.1)$$

Now we apply conservation of energy to the motion of the water on the surface (as demonstrated by the motion of the cork). The *Law of Conservation of Energy* is one of the basic principles of physics and can be stated as: *The total energy of a closed system is constant in amount.* A "closed" system simply means that no energy is allowed to enter or leave the system with respect to its surroundings. Clearly, energy cannot be conserved, i.e., fixed in amount, in a system where one keeps putting energy in from outside, for example. The real impact of this law is that energy cannot be created or destroyed; it can only move from one place or form to another. All energy that we use comes from somewhere else, or another form. This law has never been seen to be violated; it is a statement of fact about our physical universe.

In any event, let us apply this law to a water wave. The two energies involved are the energy associated with motion, the so-called kinetic energy, calculated as $\frac{1}{2} m v^2$, and the gravitational potential energy, calculated as mgh. The Law of Conservation of Energy tells us that the difference in the motional (kinetic) energy must be equal to the difference in the potential energy. The easiest way to analyze this situation is to employ a device used by the English physicist Lord Rayleigh (1842 – 1919). The trick is to consider what you would see if the wave was moving in a current which had exactly the velocity, v, of the wave, but was moving in the opposite direction. This "adverse current" enables you to concentrate on the local motion of the water at the surface in its circular path as the wave passes by. Because the adverse current is in the opposite direction to the motion of the wave, the motion of the water, in this situation, at the crest is $v - u$, and in the trough it is $v + u$. The energy equation is then,

Change in Potential Energy = Change in Kinetic Energy

$$2\,m\,g\,A \;=\; m/2\,[\,(v+u)^2 - (v-u)^2\,],$$

where the height change, h, is the vertical distance between the trough and the crest, which is $2A$, twice the amplitude of the wave. Simplifying the right-hand side, we have

$$2\,m\,g\,A \;=\; 2\,m\,v\,u,$$

or just,

$$g\,A \;=\; v\,u. \qquad (1.2)$$

Now using the result from equation 1.1 above that

$$u \;=\; A\,(\,2\,\pi/\lambda\,)\,v,$$

we have

$$g\,A \;=\; A\,(\,2\,\pi/\lambda\,)\,v^2.$$

Solving for v, the speed of the wave, yields,

$$v \;=\; \sqrt{g\,\lambda/2\,\pi},$$

or

$$v \;=\; \sqrt{g/2\,\pi}\,\sqrt{\lambda}. \qquad (1.3)$$

Equation 1.3 shows that the speed of a surface water wave is determined completely by its wavelength, i.e., the square root of the wavelength, since the first square root involves only known constants.

This result can also be obtained in other ways and has been verified experimentally. It is interesting and important not only for determining the maximum speed of displacement boats, but in a variety of different situations. For example, it is this feature of surface water waves that enables surfers to enjoy very large waves from a storm out to sea. Specifically, because the long-wavelength waves travel faster than the shorter-wavelength waves, they reach the shoreline sooner and surfers can enjoy the long rollers for a day or two before the smaller, choppier waves appear. Ocean sailors have known for centuries that an approaching storm is signaled by long rollers and that the direction of the storm is the same as the direction from which the waves are coming.

This is also why the ocean is often full of swells, i.e., waves with fairly long wavelengths. The long-wavelength waves spread out from a storm and often are able to travel very long distances without a great deal of dissipation while the shorter-wavelength waves, which take longer to travel large distances, dissipate before getting very far.

Note that this latter phenomenon is a result of the fact that shorter-wavelength waves have more energy for the same wave height compared to a longer-wavelength wave causing a greater "shearing" of the water molecules as they move about within the wave. This in turn causes the wave to dissipate energy faster. The behaviors of waves with different wavelengths can be seen even in the waves that spread out from a pebble dropped in a pond. If you look carefully, you will see that the waves that move out the fastest are those with the longer wavelength, and that they slowly spread out from the shorter wavelength ones as they go, until they all die away. At large distances, only the longest waves are still observed. A photograph of such a case is shown in Figure 1.3.

Figure 1.3 Waves produced by a stone thrown into a pond. (From R. Tricker, *Bores, Breakers, Waves and Wakes*.) Note that the longer wavelength waves move out faster than the shorter wavelength waves, because of the fact that water waves have faster speeds for longer wavelengths.

We now can understand mathematically why the wave pattern along the side of the boat develops as shown in Figure 1.1. First, we note that since the bow wave is created by the boat pushing through the water, the crest of this wave *must* move with the speed of the boat since this is how it is made. If we dictate the speed of a wave, then equation 1.3 tells us what its wavelength is, viz.,

$$\lambda = v^2 \ / \ 2\pi g.$$

This then will be the *length* of the wave seen to move back along the side of the boat. As the boat goes faster, the bow crest moves faster and the length of the wave must increase. As discussed above, the length of the wave will continue to increase as the boat speed increases until the wavelength equals the length of the boat and the stern begins to fall into the trough. This speed then is the hull speed.

Using the formula of equation 1.3, we can calculate the speed of a water wave for different wavelengths. These speeds will then determine the hull speeds for boats. For example, in the English system of units,

$$\sqrt{g \ / \ 2 \ \pi} = (\ 32 \ \text{ft/sec}^2 \ / \ 2 \ \pi)^{1/2}$$

$$= 2.26 \ \text{ft}^{1/2} \ / \ \text{sec},$$

and if the wavelength, λ, is in feet, we have for equation 1.3,

$$v = 2.26 \sqrt{\lambda} \ \ (\text{ft} / \text{sec}),$$

or,

$$v = 1.53 \sqrt{\lambda} \ (\text{mi} / \text{hr}),$$

or, using that 1 knot = 1.15 mi/hr,

$$v = 1.34 \sqrt{\lambda} \ (\text{knots}). \qquad (1.4)$$

In Table 1.1 we present the wave speeds for different wavelengths in feet/sec, mph and knots. Since the hull speed of a boat is equal to the speed of a water wave with length equal to the waterline length of a boat, these speeds are also hull speeds for boats with waterline length equal to the wavelengths indicated.

Table 1.1   Wave/Hull Speeds

Wavelength (feet)	(ft/sec)	Speed Mph	Knots (1knot= 1.15 mph)
1	2.3	1.6	1.4
5	5.0	3.4	3.0
10	7.1	4.8	4.2
20	10.1	6.9	6.0
30	12.4	8.5	7.4
50	16.0	10.0	9.5
75	19.5	13.3	11.6
100	22.6	15.4	13.4
200	31.9	21.8	18.9
300	39.1	26.7	23.2

We see that the hull speed, given by equation 1.4 and presented in Table 1.1, is less than 10 knots for most sailboats. As discussed above, the only way to get around this limit is to make the boat plane, or ride *on top* of the water, rather than plough through it. Multihulls can often do this, as can high-performance skiffs and dinghies. An ordinary monohull sailboat can do this occasionally, for example when surfing on a fairly large wave. But most of the time, when cruising sailboats run into this limit, that's as fast as they can go.

Figure 1.4 shows the resistance curve for a typical cruising sailboat as a function of the boat speed in which the hull speed indicated is calculated from equation 1.4 above. At low speeds the resistance is dominated by the surface resistance of the hull, but at higher speeds the "wave resistance," i.e., the effect discussed here, begins to dominate and finally increases sharply, effectively limiting the speed of the boat. In fact, this resistance is so great that adding more power, whether from sails or an engine, really doesn't do much good.

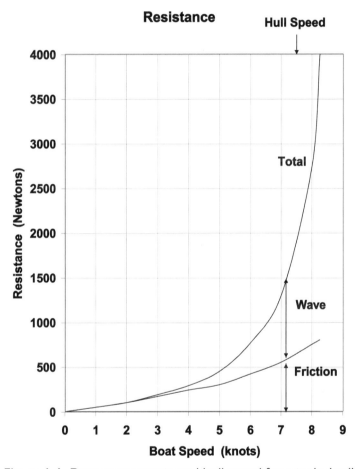

Figure 1.4 Drag components and hull speed for a typical sail-boat with waterline length of 30 feet. The drag, or resistance, is seen to rise sharply when the boat speed moves past the theoretical hull speed, where the resistance due to the wave formation along the hull becomes dominant.

In Figure 1.5 we see a photo of a sailboat moving at its hull speed. The wave, with a crest at the bow and at the stern, is seen clearly. If more power is available, it will increase the speed of the boat, the wave will become longer and the stern of the boat will fall down into the trough. The boat will then be angled up at the bow and will start to plough through the water. The resistance will increase dramatically and it will be difficult for the boat to go faster.

Another interesting example of this effect is seen when a beginner tries to learn how to swim the butterfly stroke. As the swimmer starts to windmill his arms, a wave forms in front of his body and the

Figure 1.5 A sailboat moving at hull speed. Note the wave crests at the bow and at the stern, with a well-formed trough in between. *(Photo by Greg Green, with permission.)*

swimmer feels like he is swimming uphill. The resistance is almost overwhelming. However, if the swimmer can put on a real burst of effort, he can "bust through" the wave and begin to plane. Suddenly, the swimming becomes much faster and, surprisingly, much easier. This experience is much the same as that experienced by a displacement type boat reaching its hull speed.

That the length of a boat was the major limit to its maximum speed was recognized early on both by sailors and designers. Bigger ships were generally faster than smaller ships. The fastest clipper ships, for example, were all very long. This was also true in sailboat racing at the highest levels. The America's Cup racers of the late 1800s and early 1900s kept getting longer and longer in order to obtain more speed, with the result that the limit in length was determined primarily by the size of the pocketbook of the sponsors. The race turned into a competition between multimillionaires. Finally, the competitors decided that the race should be between boats of similar size in order to emphasize sailing ability, as well as boat design. They devised a formula that put a limit on the size, shape and sail area of the boats by requiring that the square root of the sail area plus the length of the boat be less than a certain amount. Eventually, the formula became more complicated and included terms for the weight, width and other design characteristics. But the basic idea stayed the same—to limit the length.

By including the sail area and other specifications in the formula, it gave boat designers some room for improvements in boat designs, which they did, improving hull shapes, sail shapes, keel designs and other things. Many of these improvements have carried over to recreational sailing, including predominantly cruising-type boats, to the benefit of the sport overall.

In fact, many modern sailboats are now able to achieve hull speeds that are somewhat greater than the speed of the wave with wavelength equal to the waterline length of the boat. They do this by using a combination of sleek hull designs that do not generate a bow wave with very much height, and hull and keel shapes that help the boat rise out of the water a little bit at higher speeds. Both of these help to reduce the effect of wave resistance as the boat speed tries to go above its normal hull speed. Many modern racing monohulls are able to achieve hull speeds that can be up to or even greater than 1.5 times the speed of a water wave with wavelength equal to the waterline length of the boat. However, they cannot eliminate this resistance entirely and, ultimately, are limited by it.

Let us now consider the other major forms of resistance that a sailboat experiences. These are surface friction, shape or form resistance, and "induced drag." Let us consider these in turn, starting with surface resistance.

1.2 Surface Resistance

Every boat experiences resistance as it moves through the water due to the need to move the hull surface area through the water and the fact that the water molecules immediately on the surface of the hull will be attached to the hull and even move with it. This is not obvious, but it is true. The situation is analogous to that of the dust particles on the hood of a car that stay there, even when the car is moving very fast. If you go out and wipe the dust with even a very gentle touch, you will find that the dust is not really stuck on the car at all. Instead, very small intermolecular forces between the dust particles and the metal of the car are causing the dust particles to cling to the surface ever so slightly. In other words, the surface of the car or of a boat hull has air or water molecules attached to it that move with the car or boat.

The problem, in terms of boat speed, is that beyond a certain distance from the hull, the surrounding water is no longer moving with the hull. A transition must occur between the molecules moving along with the surface of the hull and the still molecules of the surrounding water. As is the case with waves, this transition results in a "shearing" of the water and involves breaking the small intermolecular forces between the water molecules called "Van der Waals' forces," after the Dutch physicist who studied and characterized them.

These forces are electrical in nature and arise because most molecules, even those that are neutral overall, are "polarized." Specifically, they have one end that is somewhat negatively charged and another end that is somewhat positively charged so that they naturally line up with the positive end of one next to the negative end of another, since unlike charges attract.

Even though the force between any two water molecules is very small, there are a very large number of molecules, something along the order of Avogadro's number, which is 6×10^{23}, even for just a few grams. This is a very large number, and the total force between such a large number of molecules is considerable.

Note that this shearing does not happen all at once, i.e., in one layer of molecules, but instead occurs over a distance of a few inches, the exact distance depending on the speed, size and shape of the boat. This shearing of the molecular bonds costs energy and is what we call *surface friction*, something that is present at all speeds. It increases with speed, since more such bonds are being broken per second. But it is at low speeds that this resistance, while small, is often the dominate resistance that the boat experiences since the other forms of resistance are even smaller. This shearing of water molecules is illustrated in Figure 1.6, which shows a plot of the speed of the water molecules relative to the hull surface for a boat moving at 5 knots.

It is important to recognize that the surface friction that a hull experiences is a qualitatively different sort of friction than that experienced between two surfaces rubbing together. For two surfaces in contact, friction arises in large part due to the

Molecular Shearing

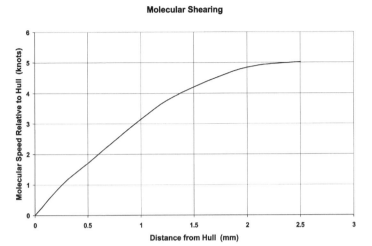

Figure 1.6   Speed of water molecules relative to the hull as one moves out from the hull, for a boat moving at 5 knots. The fact that these speeds increase indicates that shearing of water molecules must be occurring. The speed is limited at 5 knots, the speed of the boat; these molecules are sitting still with respect to the distant water. (Adapted from *The Symmetry of Sailing*, by R. Garrett.)

roughness of the surfaces, since roughness produces points that "catch" on each other and impede any motion between the two surfaces. For a hull moving through water, however, roughness comes into play in only a secondary way, since friction for a hull moving through water is due to the shearing of the water itself and is not due to high points on the hull catching on high points in the water.

It's true that roughness on the hull can cause added resistance as the hull moves through the water, but this is because it can cause turbulence in the flow of the water. Turbulence in the water carries kinetic energy with it (the energy associated with motion as discussed above for the hull speed derivation), and this energy must come from whatever is trying to move the boat through the water, whether it be sail or engine power. Of course, turbulence is to be avoided as much as possible in order to more efficiently use the power available. And in fact, a smooth hull moving slowly through water can proceed without producing turbulence. Still, as the speed is increased, turbulence will eventually be produced no matter how smooth the surface. And while a rough surface on the hull will generally cause this turbulence to begin at a lower speed and make for more turbulence at higher speeds, a small amount of roughness on a hull really has no effect on producing turbulence sooner.

The flow of water past a surface without turbulence is called *laminar flow*. Resistance in laminar flow is directly proportional to the amount of wetted surface area. This needs to be taken into account when designing hulls, keels and rudders. For a given amount of volume to be enclosed, a spherical surface has the minimum area. So if you want a maximum amount of volume in the hull for carrying cargo or just room for living, a spherical hull, i.e., a ball, or half a ball, would provide the maximum room with the least amount of surface area. Unfortunately, such a shape would not be streamlined and would produce a lot of *shape resistance*, our next topic of discussion. For now, suffice it to say that a designer must strike a balance between these two competing factors and that the correct balance will depend on whether he is more interested in room or speed, and how much so.

1.3 Shape Resistance

Clearly a more streamlined hull shape passes through water with less resistance than does a wide-beamed or very deep hull. This is because a boat with a wide beam or deep hull deflects more water off to the side than does a boat with a narrow, shallow hull, and it requires energy to do this. As is the case with all things sailing, this energy must come from the energy obtained from the wind in the sails.

Up until the latter part of the 20th century, it was considered necessary to have a fairly long, deep keel in order to prevent side-slipping in a cross wind. Such keels often helped to provide more room below deck, depending on how they were constructed and designed. With the increased recognition of the lifting power of a well-designed keel, however, it was realized that a narrow keel could be quite effective. The result is that if you simply want a very fast boat, you can use a narrow, shallow hull with a narrow, but deep keel, usually with a bulb on the bottom to reduce turbulence and increase righting moment. Such a boat is not the best boat for cruising, of course, because it will not have a lot of room below for living and a deep keel limits use in shallow water. Again, a compromise must be accepted that tries to provide a fair amount of room and yet has reasonable streamlining.

Down through the years, many different shapes have been used in sailboat hull design. For some time, people thought that a fairly bulbous bow with a long narrow stern was the ideal shape. This hull shape was referred to as having a "mackerel" bow and a "cod" tail, since these fish have these shapes. Isaac Newton even weighed in on the subject and discussed what he called the optimum hull shape in his famous book *The Mathematical Principles of Natural Philosophy*, usually just referred to as the "Principia." The shape he recommended was an ellipsoid (a 3-D ellipse) with a truncated cone attached at the bow.

Since the advent of wind tunnels and water tanks, it is now possible to try different designs and see which actually present less resistance to a given current. Sophisticated computer codes also exist that can test the different design shapes theoretically. But these tests are not unambiguous, since small changes in bow, stern, and keel designs often interact with each other in less-than-obvious ways.

The general conclusion, at this time, is that the shape with least form resistance is one with a fairly narrow bow and a wider stern that both provides a reasonable amount of room below and promotes surfing. Shallow hulls also have been shown to have less resistance than deeper hulls and are easier to make plane.

Note that for a cruising boat, the designer usually starts by deciding how much headroom is absolutely required and then making the hull deep enough to accommodate this. The stern design is important because if the stern is too wide and ends too abruptly, it will produce strong turbulence in the form of eddies behind the boat. These eddies can actually pull backwards on the boat. We will discuss this more in the next section on induced resistance. The design of a modern racing hull for a monohull sailing boat is shown in Figure 1.7.

An actual photograph of the hull of a modern, racing monohull sailboat is shown in Figure 1.8. It has a narrow bow, a relatively flat, shallow bottom,

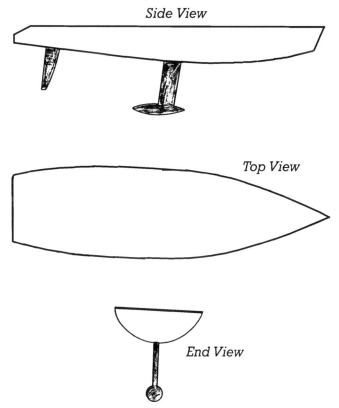

Side View

Top View

End View

Figure 1.7 Design of hull shape for a modern racing monohull sailboat, ca. 2000.

Figure 1.8 The hull of ILLBRUCK, winner of the 2001-2002 Volvo Ocean Race as an example of a modern, racing, mono-hulled sailboat. Note the narrow bow, the relatively flat bottom, and the truncated stern, and also the narrow, deep keel with a large bulb at the bottom. *(Photo by Rick Tomlinson, with permission.)*

a wide stern and a deep, narrow keel. We will discuss this final element in even greater detail in the next chapter.

1.4 Parasitic Resistance

Besides surface resistance and wave-making resistance, resistance comes from turbulence created in the water as it flows along the hull, from eddies produced behind the boat, and from vortices generated at the bottom of the keel and rudder. The resistance from the vortices created behind the keel and rudder is called "induced drag" and will be discussed in the next chapter on keels. For now, let us discuss the resistance obtained from the other two kinds of turbulence. We will start by considering how turbulence is formed in water as it flows along the hull.

Normally, the flow of water past the hull begins without turbulence. However, not very far along the hull, usually only a few feet back, it begins. The point at which this happens is determined by the speed of the boat and the roughness of the hull. As indicated above, as water moves along the surface of even the smoothest hulls, the shearing of the water that occurs will introduce motions in the water perpendicular to the general flow along the hull. This perpendicular motion will then provide a twisting effect in the water that, when it becomes large enough, will produce turbulence. If the hull is long enough, turbulence will eventually be formed at almost any speed or roughness. Similarly, more speed will produce turbulence sooner, as will a rough surface.

Let us start our discussion of turbulence by considering that we have a very smooth hull, in which case the combined effect of speed and length for producing turbulence can be expressed in a quantity known as the *Reynold's number*, named for Osborne Reynolds, an English engineer who studied turbulence in the late 1800s.

What Reynolds found was that turbulence always occurs when the product of the length, *L*, and the speed, *v*, divided by the ratio of the viscosity to the density of the fluid, is equal to about 1 million. This is true for motion through any fluid, including both water and air. (We will use this result also when we discuss sails, in Chapter 3.) Mathematically, Reynold's number is

$$R = (L\,v)\,/\,(\mu\,/\,\rho)\,,\qquad(1.5)$$

where μ is the viscosity, and ρ is the density. Viscosity is a measure of the amount of force necessary to shear a fluid. It is defined as the ratio of the force per unit area required to produce a unit change of velocity per unit distance perpendicular to the flow, i.e., it is defined from the equation,

$$\tau = \mu\,(\Delta v\,/\,\Delta y)\,,\qquad(1.6)$$

where τ is the stress, or force, per unit area, v is the velocity, and y is the direction perpendicular to the velocity (flow), e.g., out from the surface of the hull. The Greek letter "Δ" stands for "change in." We see that a more viscous fluid requires more force per unit area for a given velocity change than does a less viscous fluid. This is just the statement that it is harder to pull something through molasses than it is through water. Ideally, the viscosity, μ, is measured as the force required when moving two very large parallel plates past each other in the fluid, at a given velocity, separated by a measured distance.

As discussed above, the molecules of the fluid will be stationary with respect to each plate, immediately next to each plate. If the plates are moving with respect to each other, some shearing of the fluid must occur between the two plates. Some fluids are more viscous than others, i.e., the inter-molecular forces are greater in some fluids than others. Experiments can be devised to measure the viscosity of a given fluid quite accurately, e.g., by rotating one cylinder inside another cylinder with the fluid in between the cylinders.

The viscosity of water is measured to be 1.0×10^{-3} N • sec / m². "N" stands for "Newton," the unit of force in the metric system. The density of water is 1 gm/cm³, or 10^3 kg/m³. Hence, in equation 1.6 above, using these values for the viscosity and density, we have that the Reynold's number is

$$R = (L\ v\ ) / (\ 10^{-6}\ ),\ \text{or}$$

$$R = (L\ v\ )\ 10^6,$$

with L in m and v in m/sec. As indicated above, Reynolds found that turbulence will always start when this number is about 10^6. Hence this will occur when the product $L\ v$ is about unity. If we are concerned with a sailboat moving at about 5 knots, which is 2.4 m/sec, then turbulence will begin when $L = 0.4$ m, or in a little more than 1 foot. At 10 knots, turbulence will begin when $L = 0.2$ m, or in less than one foot. We see that turbulence is almost always produced as a hull moves through the water; it is only when the boat is moving very slowly, that no turbulence will be produced.

The usual situation is shown in Figure 1.9. The flow of the water starts with *laminar*, or non-turbulent, flow at the bow, and then a foot or so back the flow begins to be turbulent. Note that most of this turbulence is confined to a small area along the hull and that the resistance with turbulence is typically four to five times greater than it is when the flow is laminar.

The ratio of the turbulent resistance to the non-turbulent resistance depends on the velocity and increases with higher velocities. Exactly what the turbulent resistance is for a boat depends on the shape of the boat as well as the velocity, and this resistance must actually be measured.

Computer codes exist that try to model the motion of a hull through water, and they can be used to provide a reasonable prediction of the resistance of a hull shape through water at different speeds. But these kinds of measurements and computer predictions are beyond the scope of what we want to do here. Again, our goal is to try to understand what is happening. By understanding, we can appreciate what has gone into the design of a boat and make better use of the capabilities of the boat. If you want to actually design a new boat, whether for racing or recreation, you can start with

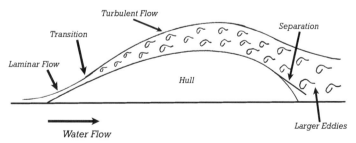

Figure 1.9 Water flow along a hull.

some of the references provided at the end of this book.

A few words more about the effect of roughness on drag are now appropriate. If there are large bumps or objects attached to the hull, clearly these will produce increased resistance since they will deflect water to the side, which costs energy. However, even fairly small bumps can begin to create more resistance simply because they will cause turbulence to form sooner and possibly be more pronounced, while a smooth hull will postpone the onset of turbulence and keep the drag lower. Turbulence will still form at any reasonable speed in a few feet along the surface of the hull.

The question then becomes, how smooth is smooth enough? Hydrodynamic testing shows that a surface in water is "smooth" if it has no bumps larger than about 0.05 mm, or 0.002 in. This size does depend somewhat on the speed of the hull, but this is good for most hull speeds for sailing boats and can be achieved by a good sanding of the hull followed by a coat or two of good marine hull paint.

If you desire to make the hull even smoother, by all means feel free to do so, but it will not significantly decrease the resistance of the hull through the water. Sailors often observe that the antifouling paints used on hulls are not very glossy. But this is okay since the smoothness is good enough and the chemicals in the paint that make barnacles stay off are the important thing. Barnacles, obviously, are bumps that are larger than 0.05 mm and will significantly increase the surface resistance of the hull.

Over the years, people have tried lots of things to reduce the surface drag of hulls, including waxing and polishing, high-gloss paints and even oil coatings. But ultimately these steps have very minimal value and are really not necessary. In other words, getting a hull down to the smoothness of a good sanding with a coat of hull paint is important; any further smoothing is not. Of course, racing boats, with a large financial investment, will often do everything possible to gain even the tiniest amount of extra speed. Hence they are usually painted with high-gloss paint and cleaned and waxed much more often.

Let us now consider the other turbulence associated with the motion of a hull through the water that is left in the wake. As a boat moves through the water, it can form a pocket of reduced pressure in the water immediately behind the stern. The flowing water will be pulled into this pocket and form still more eddies, resulting in another form of turbulence or resistance.

This sort of thing happens to other objects moving through fluids as well, including cars and airplanes moving through air. With race cars you see various attempts at reducing this induced drag. Cars are often equipped with "spoilers" that attempt to deflect some air into the pocket to increase the pressure there. Many modern race cars can also be found with square or truncated rear ends that attempt to break up the kind of eddy pattern that can be produced behind the car.

For sailboats, it is almost always preferable to have a fairly tapered stern in order to try to minimize these eddies since they don't have the power of an internal combustion engine when under sail. It's true that many modern racing sailboats have truncated sterns, but the truncation occurs above the waterline where it has no effect on the production of eddy patterns behind the boat.

Figure 1.8 above shows a picture of the yacht ILL-BRUCK, which was the winner of the 2001-2002 Volvo Ocean Race. It has a hull shape that is very tapered in the front to reduce form resistance, relatively narrow and shallow to help reduce form resistance and help with planing, and a stern that is truncated above the waterline. The hull actually becomes quite flat near the stern, and this shape helps the boat to plane more easily even as it comes out of the water gradually so that no more trailing eddies are formed than necessary. The exact design for hulls on racing boats like this are determined from computer modeling and tank testing with scaled models.

The boats in the 2001-2002 Volvo Ocean Race were often able to average speeds in high winds of around 20 knots for extended times. This is a speed that is about two times the hull speeds for these boats and is obtained by planing, or actually riding on top of the bow wave. This kind of performance in strong wind conditions is very impressive for a monohulled sailboat. Most cruising monohulls are unable to do this.

2

Keels

Following our discussion of hulls, let us continue below the waterline and discuss the physics of keels. Keels and sails work in a somewhat similar fashion, and the basic physics principles are much the same, even though one operates in water and the other in air. It is perhaps a little easier to understand some of the basic principles in discussing how a keel works. It will then be possible to see how these same principles are at work with sails, where it is initially not so obvious that these principles are involved.

A keel is anything extending downward along the underside of the hull, even if it is only a small ridge along the centerline. Usually, on a modern sailboat the keel extends significantly down below the bottom of the hull. There are two principal

purposes for a keel on a sailboat. The first is to prevent side-slipping when the wind is from the side.
The second is to provide a counterbalance to help
reduce heeling as the wind blows on the sails from
the side. Let us discuss these two roles in order.

It was undoubtedly recognized from the earliest
attempts to sail a boat that something was needed
when the wind came from the side to keep the boat
from being pushed sideways. Over the centuries the
solutions to this problem have been many, depending on the characteristics and types of sailing being
done in various locales. In fact, most of these solutions continue to be used on at least some sailboats
somewhere in the world.

These solutions include using a long, shallow
"full" keel running along the centerline of the
hull, centerboards or daggerboards lowered vertically into the water either through the hull itself
or off to the sides, or fins attached along the bottom of the hull. The "fin" keel is by far the most
common solution on modern sailboats, and it is
the physics of the fin keel that we will discuss here
(generally a keel will mean a fin keel). Note, however, that most of this discussion also applies to
longer, shallower keels and certainly to deep, thin
daggerboards.

2.1 Bernoulli's Principle and Lift

Clearly any kind of fin or board placed vertically into
the water with its plane parallel to the long axis of

the boat will provide resistance to moving sideways. This was recognized from early on. Only since the development of air flight, however, has it been recognized that a properly designed keel can actually provide "lift," i.e., a positive force in the direction *into* the wind. Here we will discuss how this is possible and how to best design keels to maximize this effect.

Even though some readers may be aware of the basic principle of flight for an airplane wing, let us review it here. The Swiss mathematician Jakob Bernoulli discovered in the late 17th century that the pressure of a fluid decreases as the speed of flow of the fluid increases. His son, Daniel, was then able to obtain an equation quantitatively relating the pressure and velocity of the fluid.

The common demonstration that this is true involves blowing along the top of a thin strip of paper held in your fingers. As you blow, the strip of paper, which normally is drooping, will rise as it is sucked up into the region of reduced pressure in the fast-moving air coming out of your mouth. (Try it, it works!) This result follows directly from the Law of Conservation of Energy, which was discussed in Chapter 1.

In the optional box below, we obtain the mathematical statement of Bernoulli's principle. As with other optional sections, this can be skipped without losing any of the understanding of the general discussion. It is included here for those readers who would like to see a derivation of this principle, which plays such an important role in how keels and sails actually work.

To illustrate Bernoulli's Principle, we will use a variation of the Law of Conservation of Energy known as the *Work-Energy Theorem*. This theorem recognizes that one way to change the energy of a system is to do "work" on a system and that the work done on a system must equal the change in energy of the system. Work is defined as force x distance. (Note that it takes energy to do work, so you do not create new energy by doing work.) The energy of the system that is changing for a wing or keel is the energy associated with motion, called the *kinetic energy*, and is calculated as ½ *mv²*. Pressure is force per unit area, so force is pressure x area. Work then is pressure (P) x area (A) x distance (S). Area x distance is volume (V). Mathematically we have,

Work Done = Change in Kinetic Energy

$$\Delta P \times A \times S = \Delta \left(\tfrac{1}{2} mv^2 \right),$$
where Δ stands for "change in".

Since A (area) x S (distance) = V (volume), and m (the mass of air molecules) is constant, we have

$$\Delta P \times V = \tfrac{1}{2} m \, \Delta (v^2),$$

and dividing through by the volume, V, yields

$$\Delta P = \tfrac{1}{2} \rho \, \Delta (v^2), \quad (2.1)$$

where $\rho = m/V$ is the density of the fluid. Hence, we see that a change in pressure is related to a change in the velocity; and vice versa, a change in the velocity is related to a change in the pressure.

Equation 2.1 obtained in the optional box tells us that the application of the work-energy theorem leads directly to the result that a change in pressure leads to a change in the velocity. (Actually we see that the change is in the square of the velocity. But if the square is to change, the velocity itself must change.) This is what you would expect, even on general physical intuition. The *really* interesting part, however, is that the equation works both ways! In other words, if there is a change in the velocity of the fluid, then there must have been a change in the pressure. This is Bernoulli's principle.

A classic airplane wing uses this principle in order to obtain lift. The wing is designed to have a longer path along the top surface than along the bottom surface, as shown in Figure 2.1. Because of the pressure of the air from in front of and around the wing, the flow of air over the top will have a larger speed in order to try to keep pace with the air moving past the wing. This increase in speed will then result in a decrease of pressure along the top of the wing.

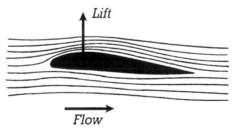

Fig. 2.1 Air flow around a wing. The bump in the air flow over the top of the wing makes for a longer path and the air will travel faster to try to keep up. This increased speed on the top produces less pressure and results in lift, as indicated.

Because the pressure is greater on the bottom of the wing than it is on the top, the wing is pushed upward; this is what is called lift.

Actually, it is not necessary for a wing to be asymmetrical like the classic wing shape shown in Figure 2.1, since you can accomplish the same thing by using a symmetrical wing inclined at an angle to the oncoming wind. This angle is referred to as the "angle of attack." As shown in Figure 2.2, having an angle of attack will also cause the air moving over the top surface to travel a longer path and thereby speed up. (Alternatively, you could say that the air proceeding along the bottom of the wing gets to take a shortened path.) The increased speed of the air over the top of the wing will produce a reduced pressure, i.e., a bit of a vacuum, just as before, and the wing will experience lift. Most modern planes, especially faster-moving planes like jets, have nearly symmetrical wing shapes and obtain lift in part by using an angle of attack. Planes that move relatively slowly often will use the classical, more asymmetri-

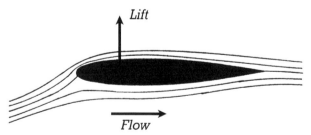

Figure 2.2 Air flow around a symmetrical wing with an angle of attack to the air flow. The air flow over the top still has a longer path to follow and will move faster, producing lift by Bernoulli's principle.

cal shape in order to achieve more lift at all angles of attack.

Keels, of course, must be symmetrical, since boats need to be able to move with the wind approaching from either the starboard or port side. Hence, like a modern jet, a keel works by having an angle of attack. In fact, the wing shown in Figure 2.2 could just as well be a keel. If you look at how a sailboat moves with the wind coming from the side, you will indeed find that the keel will be moving through the water at an angle so as to have an angle of attack, and that this angle of attack will be such that the side with the faster flow, and hence the lift, will be on the side where the wind is coming from! This is shown in Figure 2.3, in which the wind is coming from the port side about 30 degrees off the bow.

In this figure, we also show the wind moving past the sail and the net force or lift that is derived from this flow. (We will discuss how the sail obtains this lift in more detail in the next chapter, but basically it also does this according to Bernoulli's principle as discussed above.) Note that the boat does not move directly in the direction in which it is pointed (which is also the direction of the symmetry axis of its keel), but rather it will move with a "sidle" type of motion called *leeway* (somewhat exaggerated in the figure). It is this sidling motion that causes the keel to have an angle of attack.

As shown in the figure, the side with the longer path for the flowing water, and hence the side with the lift, is on the side toward the direction of the wind. This results in a force on the boat in that direction. Of course, the wind is also blowing against the sails from that side, which produces a force on the boat in the other direction, so that in equilibrium, these two sideways forces just balance each other. At the same time, because the sails are at an angle with respect to the wind from abeam, there is also a forward component of force from the wind on the sails

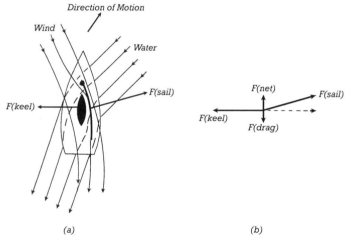

(a)   *(b)*

Figure 2.3 Balance between lift from air flow around the sail and water flow around the keel for a boat moving about 30° away from the wind direction. Part (a) shows the wind flowing past the sail and the water flowing around the keel; the forces from the sail and keel are shown as the indicated vectors (arrows). Part (b) shows the force vectors (arrows) alone and how they combine. The dashed arrow is that component of the force on the sail that just balances the force on the keel. The upward arrow is the net force from the sail and keel combined. The downward arrow in (b) is the drag, or resistance, of the boat as it moves through the water. At constant speed, all these forces just balance each other.

that will propel the boat forward. The forces involved are shown without the boat in part B. Note that the forward component of the force on the sails is shown as the small arrow pointing upward.

As the boat moves faster, the lift from the keel increases and the need for a large keel is actually reduced. Therefore, it is in low-wind situations that a large keel is more necessary. Indeed, in very low-wind situations, most sailboats will slowly drift downwind since the keel cannot generate enough lift to counteract the force of the wind against the sails. This might lead you to think that it would always help to have a large keel. But remember, a large keel also provides more surface area, which results in more resistance to motion. And this resistance is not insignificant. In fact, at low speeds, the total surface friction of a sailboat in the water is the dominating resistance that the boat encounters.

Figure 2.4 An example of a long keel of the type generally used on sailboats before the 1970s. Some people still prefer such keels because they often provide a larger righting moment and work better in light-wind situations.

Anything you can do to reduce this resistance is a real help in increasing the speed of the boat. Therefore, modern sailboats typically have relatively small keels compared to older sailboats. This trend is shown in Figure 2.5.

Sailboats from the 19th century almost always had long, full keels. This was considered necessary to prevent side-slipping from the pressure of the wind in the sails. The idea that a keel could produce lift was not recognized. As the 20th century progressed, airplanes were developed and the idea of lift by a wing was appreciated. This recognition was slowly applied to keels on sailboats with the result that designers realized they could considerably reduce keel size and yet still get plenty of lift, especially at higher wind speeds.

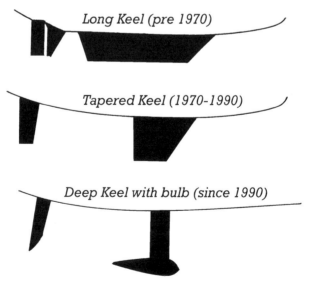

Figure 2.5 Evolution of keel shapes during the 20th century.

Fig. 2.6 An example of a tapered keel on a 1980s cruising-type sailboat.

As it was recognized that smaller keels worked fine and resulted in faster boats, designers refined the exact shape that a good keel should have. In order to understand these refinements, we need to consider wing theory in a little more detail. As mentioned earlier, this discussion will also be applicable in the next chapter for understanding how sails work.

2.2 Vortex Formation

As a wing generates lift, it also produces turbulence in the form of a vortex off its end, and this vortex costs energy. In order to understand how this happens, consider Figure 2.7. The angle of attack produces the higher speed and lower pressure on one side of the keel. This lower pressure on one side re-

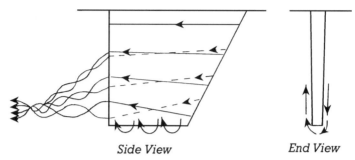

Side View   End View

Fig. 2.7 Vortex formation at the bottom and rear of a keel. Because of the difference in pressure on the two sides of the keel, as explained by Bernoulli's principle, there will be a net flow from the high pressure side of the keel to the low pressure side. The flowing backward along the keel as the boat moves forward will then slope downward on the high pressure side and upward on the low pressure side. When these flows meet coming off the rear of the keel, the water flow will be twisted, forming vortices.

sults in a net flow of water around the tip of the keel from the high pressure side to the low pressure side, as shown in the end view in Figure 2.7. This water does not flow directly downward or upward, but somewhat downward on one side and somewhat upward on the other side as it flows mostly backward thanks to the motion of the keel forward through the water. This is what is shown in the side view.

Note that when these flows meet at the trailing edge of the keel, one side is sloped downward and the other side is sloped upward. The result is a twisting effect on the flow of water off the back of the keel, which becomes more pronounced closer to the tip of the keel and results in a very turbulent flow that forms vortices. These vortices tend to combine together to form one larger vortex, and the formation of this vortex costs energy. The energy lost this way is referred to as induced resistance or *induced drag* for the keel and is similar to that caused by the induced vortices that form off airplane wings. Figures 2.8 and 2.9 show a couple of nice examples of these kinds of vortices. Similar vortices are formed at the tips of keels and also at the top and bottom of sailboat sails. We will discuss sail-generated vortices later.

The general form of air flow over an airplane wing is shown in Figure 2.10. The flow first goes up and then back down as it moves along the top surface. Note that the downward flow continues behind the wing and that it is this downward flow

Fig. 2.8 Wingtip vortex formation and downwash observed in cloud layer behind a rising airplane. *(Photo courtesy of Cessna Aircraft Co.)*

Fig. 2.9 Wingtip vortex seen from crop duster flying over a flare placed on the ground. *(Photo courtesy of NASA.)*

behind the wing called the "downwash" that is really the effect of the airplane pushing down on the air to give it the lift it needs to fly. The downwash can be seen in the depression in the cloud in the photo of Figure 2.8.

The vortices produced at the tips of the wings are also shown in Figure 2.10. These vortices cost energy and reduce the efficiency of the lift of the wing. Note that the end of the wing attached to the fuselage of the airplane or the end of the keel attached to the hull experiences no vortex simply because there is no end over which the circulation can proceed. Furthermore, the easiest way to reduce the fraction of energy lost to the tip vortices is to increase the length of the wing, since if you keep the total area of the wing fixed, there will be less induced drag for a longer, narrower wing. This follows since the tip vortex remains approximately constant, independent of the length of the wing. In fact, for a given total lift and wing area, the induced drag varies inversely with the *aspect ratio*, i.e., the ratio of the length to width of the wing. Gliders use this fact to obtain a large amount of lift with relatively little induced drag by using very long wings. Such long wings are not necessary on a powered airplane

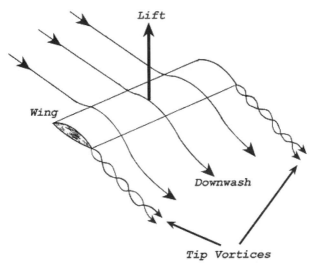

Figure 2.10 Schematic representation of air flow and vortex formation around an airplane wing. Besides the tip vortices, there is also a general down-flow of air behind the wing as the air flows over the wing. This down-flow is known as the "downwash." Fig. 2.8. shows these tip vortices and the downwash.

since the loss of energy in the tip vortex can be made up by applying more power from the engine. Long wings are inconvenient for several reasons.

Beyond the question of aspect ration, the question arises whether some *shapes* for the wing or keel will be more effective in generating lift than other shapes. In fact, it has been shown that a shape that is elliptical in distribution as it moves out along the wing, tapering to zero lift at the tip of the wing, will provide the maximum lift with the minimum amount of induced drag for a given total area of wing or keel. The derivation of this result is somewhat lengthy for presentation here and requires the use of calculus. But the interested reader can refer to various texts on wing theory, such as that by Kuethe and Chow, for an example of this derivation.

In the meantime, it is easy to see why a shape that produces a distribution like this will help, since as the wing narrows as you approach the tip, the magnitude of the induced vortex can be reduced while still maintaining a relatively large wing area. The famous World War II British Spitfire fighter planes were designed with wings that produced such an elliptical lift distribution and had elliptical shapes along their edges. Examples also exist in nature, like the many fast-moving fish with fins that are approximately elliptical in shape along one or both edges, including dolphin and shark fins.

In terms of yacht design, a good approximation to the elliptical shape can be achieved by using a simple tapered keel as shown in Figure 2.5. Most sailboats produced between about 1970 and 1990 had tapered keels like this and they have proved to be quite efficient at producing lift while minimizing surface area and induced drag. Note that these considerations for keels apply also to rudders, with the result that many modern rudders have elliptical shapes and are long, i.e., deep, or tapered in order to minimize induced drag while still being effective. In fact, most sailboats are now designed so that the rudder acts also as a second keel to help provide lift and prevent side-slipping.

Another thing that can be done to reduce the formation of the tip vortex and induced drag is to place a vane at the tip that is perpendicular to the surface of the wing or keel. On planes these are called "winglets" and on keels they are called "wings." The purpose of the winglet or wing is to try to reduce the flow around the tip from the high-pressure side to the low-pressure side and thus to reduce the resulting vortex. Such winglets are often seen on small private jet airplanes and even some small commercial jets. Look for them the next time you are at the airport.

Although wing keels were first tried on boats early in the 20th century, the current popularity of wings at the bottom of a keel is clearly due to the success of the sailboat AUSTRALIA II in the America's Cup race in 1983. This boat was the first of the 12-meter racing yachts to use such a winged keel, and it was also the first boat to beat the Americans in over 100 years. Probably most of the Australian victory was due to superior sailing by the Aussies, but it is generally considered that their wing keel was a help.

Since the dramatic victory of AUSTRALIA II, winged keels have become quite commonplace. Most of the major manufacturers of recreational cruising sailboats now use winged keels. A winged keel offers more lift with less induced drag. The wings also add more weight at the bottom of the keel, which helps keep the boat upright in a breeze (more on this below). The result is that a designer can use a keel that has a shallower draft than would be possible without the wings at the bottom, while still obtaining enough lift. This is important on recreational sailboats in order to make it possible to get in and out of shallower areas. However, if a boat with a wing keel does get stuck in a shallow area, it can sometimes be harder to extract than a traditional one! Today, most sailboat manufacturers prefer a keel that has a bit of a taper, with a bulb and/or wings at the bottom to reduce induced drag. Like the wings, the bulb helps with righting moment by placing yet more weight down low. An example of a modern winged keel used on a cruising type of sailboat is shown in Figure 2.11.

At the same time, racing sailboats continue to evolve, a process that includes advances in keel design. The present design that is prevalent for keels on large, sophisticated racing sailboats, such as for the America's Cup or for the Volvo Ocean Race, is a long narrow keel with a large bulb at the bottom, as shown at the bottom of Figure 2.5. These keels have become quite narrow and quite long. They often extend down more than 10 feet and are the nautical equivalent of the long, narrow wings on gliders. The

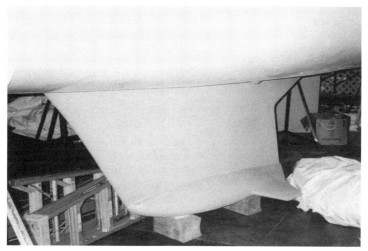

Figure 2.11 An example of a "winged keel" used on a modern cruising sailboat. Note the bulb and wings to help increase righting moment and reduce induced drag (vortices).

bulb itself may or may not have small wings on it since the bulb's presence alone helps to reduce the flow around the tip, thereby decreasing the vortex formation. Still, small wings on the bulb may help reduce this flow even more. The main purpose of the bulb is to provide more weight at the end of a long lever arm to help keep the boat more upright. An example of this kind of keel is seen in Figure 2.12 for a modern racing, monohull sailboat. This leads us now to consider the other main purpose of the keel, which is to help prevent heeling.

Fig. 2.12 The keel of the racing sailboat ILLBRUCK, winner of the 2001-2002 Volvo Ocean Race. This figure is a detail from Fig. 2.8 and an example of a modern deep keel with a large bulb at the bottom, as used on modern racing hulls. *(Photo by Rick Tomlinson, with permission.)*

2.3 Righting Moment

Sailboats move through the water with the least amount of resistance when they are upright. This is because almost all boats are wider at the deck than they are below the waterline. Specifically, because a sailboat is usually wider at the deck than below, as it heels over due to the wind blowing on the sail, the wider part of the hull is forced down into the water on the leeward, or downwind, side. This, of course, increases the form resistance. Usually, the total wetted surface area increases as well, causing that much greater surface resistance. A designer can reduce this by keeping the boat quite narrow, even at the deck level, and many racing boats try to do this as much as possible. However, this reduces the volume in the hull and makes a recreational sailboat impractical since the boat simply hasn't much space on or below deck.

Heeling has another undesirable result and that is the common effect of "weather helm," a phenomenon that both slows a boat's progress through the water and makes it more difficult to steer. This is because as a sailboat heels over, the bulging leeward side of the hull begins to be more in the water, presenting more resistance to the forward motion than the other side of the hull.

This increased resistance then acts like a rudder board placed in the water angled parallel to the bulging deck, and as this angle deflects the water it tries to move the boat around to head more into the wind, so that the farther the boat heels over, the more the helmsman has to turn the rudder to compensate. Obviously, the turned rudder adds more resistance to forward motion, and the speed of the boat suffers. Therefore you want to keep the boat as upright as possible.

In fact, there is an optimum heel angle for any given wind speed and point of sail that balances the negative effects of healing against the positive effects of carrying more sail. Sailing with the boat as close to upright as possible may be the ideal. But if you reduce the sail area too much in order to reduce heeling, you lose speed too.

Of course, a heavy keel will help to keep the

boat upright. As the boat heels over, the keel moves away from the centerline and the weight of the keel tends to right the boat. Most keels are made of lead, or at least of iron, and it is not uncommon for a third or even half the weight of a boat to be in the ballast of the keel. When looking at different designs, the so-called "righting moment" is the best measure of a keel's ability to keep a boat upright. Righting moment is calculated as the restoring force times the lever arm, with the lever arm being the distance away from the center of gravity of the boat.

The restoring force is the component of the weight of the keel that is perpendicular to the normal vertical centerline of the boat. This is the component that tends to restore the boat to its normal vertical position while the force of the wind in the sails produces a "heeling moment" that tends to tip the boat. Clearly, higher winds and taller, bigger, more powerful sails produce a larger heeling moment, and this heeling moment must be compensated for by the righting moment of the rest of the boat, especially by the keel. A deeper, heavier keel produces a larger righting moment, but as always, a compromise must be affected since a deeper keel causes problems for shallow-water cruising, and a heavier keel produces more total weight that must be propelled by the wind power in the sails.

A normal cruising sailboat usually has a very good righting moment from its keel, and one important consequence of this is that it is very difficult to turn the boat completely over. In fact, even if the boat is heeled over past 90 degrees, the weight of the keel will often be enough to right the boat. Obviously, this is not so true for daggerboard sailboats or boats without some kind of weighted keel. But for the vast majority of cruising boats this is a prerequisite of good design.

Figure 2.13 shows sample stability curves for a typical weighted keelboat, a daggerboard sailboat and for a catamaran, i.e., a double-hulled sailboat. As seen, the sailboat with the weighted keel is amazingly stable; the daggerboard boat is not as stable; and while the double-hulled sailboat is actually seen to be more stable at low heeling angle, beyond a certain angle it quickly becomes unstable. In fact, this is the general experience with multihull sailboats. In most winds, they heel over less than a monohull since about half of the weight of the boat is in each hull, and it takes a lot of wind to lift one of the hulls very far out of the water. In very heavy winds, however, a multihull can actually flip over. Additionally, when a multihull is overturned, it is quite stable that way and is very difficult to turn back over for the same reason it was stable when upright, i.e., the entire weight of one of the two hulls needs to be overcome in order to get it to heel.

An ordinary monohull, on the other hand, is inherently unstable when upside down so it doesn't usually take much effort to right it again. Clearly, as long as the weather conditions do not get too bad, multihulls are faster than monohulls. This is because multihulls, with the exception of some of the newer, heavier cruising designs, have much less resistance through the water since the two hulls can each be made much narrower than the hull on a monohull and provide much less shape resistance. They can also be made much lighter since there is no need for a ballasted keel. In fact, catamarans are fastest when one of the two hulls is just raised out of the water since this reduces the form and surface resistance even further. Most racing multihulls are actually designed to operate this way.

There is a lot of debate about the relative merits of multihulls and monohulls, in large part because they are so different in terms of performance and design. For example, while multihulls are generally faster and sail more upright, monohulls are usually cheaper for the same amount of room below deck, and in extreme weather conditions they are ultimately safer.

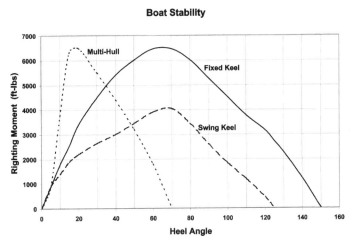

Figure 2.13 The righting moment as a function of heeling angle for typical fixed-keel and swing-keel mono-hulled sailboats, and for a catamaran multi-hulled sailboat.

Multihulls can be made safer by extending the distance between the hulls, but as indicated above, they can not be made to have a positive righting moment, i.e., one that will tend to make the boat return to an upright position beyond 90 degrees as can be the case for a monohull. Note, however, that some modern racing monohulls, for example, those used in shorthanded, long-distance events like the Vendée Globe or the Around Alone, are designed to be very wide with flat bottoms in order to plane better, and this can result in a hull shape that is also stable upside down.

For all sailboats, the form resistance and surface resistance is less when the boat is more upright. The weighted keel helps to keep the boat this way and the long, deep keels of the racing sailboats with a large bulb at the bottom are designed to do this as much as possible. For recreational sailboats, a shorter keel with weighted wings at the bottom is generally the best solution, providing reduced induced drag and less heeling than a traditional tapered keel of the same depth. Of course, increased weight in the keel for ballast also increases the amount of weight that must be propelled forward by the wind power in the sails; consequently there is a balance to be struck. This balance will be different for sailboats to be used predominantly for racing than for sailboats to be used predominantly for cruising. Most modern sailboats represent some kind of balance between designs that are fast and designs that provide a lot of room below deck and are more stable. Clearly though, modern recreational and cruising type sailboats perform significantly better than they did 50 years ago because of improved keel designs that produce more lift and better righting moment with less surface area, less total weight, and less induced drag.

2.4 Total Resistance

At this point, it is possible to sum up total resistance as a function of boat speed. At low speeds, resistance is dominated by the surface friction of the hull and keel in the water. Induced drag, i.e., vortex formation, and wave resistance are not as important. As the speed increases, however, resistance increases as turbulent flow becomes more important and increases the surface resistance. Induced drag then begins to contribute more resistance after which wave resistance becomes the largest factor in the total resistance equation. Ultimately, wave resistance completely dominates and takes off dramatically, effectively limiting the speed of the boat to some factor between one and two times the speed of a surface water wave with wavelength equal to the waterline length of the boat.

A modern racing sailboat will have a narrow, shallow hull in order to provide less shape resistance, with a deep, narrow keel to provide good lift with minimum drag. A daysailer or cruising sailboat will compromise this shape and keel design in order to provide more room below deck and have a shallower draft for sailing in shallow waters.

Keels

In Figure 2.14 we show how the different kinds of resistance all contribute to the total resistance of a typical sailboat moving through the water with a speed close to its hull speed. The two largest contributions come from the wave formation along the hull and from the total surface resistance. The latter includes turbulence formation along the hull. Each of these constitutes about one-third of the overall resistance. The remaining third is divided up between induced drag, which is responsible for about 10 percent, and everything else, sometimes called "parasitic resistance," which is responsible for about 20 percent of total resistance. The latter includes heeling resistance, roughness, eddies created behind the hull and added wave formation due to the rocking and rolling of the boat as it moves.

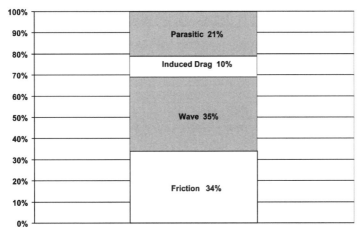

Figure 2.14 Resistance components for a typical mono-hulled sailboat moving at a speed somewhat less than hull speed.

3

Sails

We are now ready to discuss the physics of sails. As noted earlier, many of our discussions regarding the physics of the hull and of keels will be directly applicable to this subject as well, especially when looking at how sails work when sailing to windward. For example, sails obtain lift from the flow of air past them just as a keel obtains lift from the flow of water. Vortices are produced at the top of a sail just as they are at the bottom of a keel. The flow of air past the sail also results in turbulence just as the flow of water along the hull and keel does.

In short, many of the aspects of sail theory will sound very similar to some of the earlier discussions regarding hulls and keels. Of course, there will be some new ideas that we must consider as well. As usual, our interest here is to *understand* what is going on as much as possible. It will not be our intent to enable the reader to actually design sails. Our goal is to understand why designers do what they do and how different designs have certain advantages and disadvantages.

3.1 Basic Sail Theory

As is the case with modern keels, the sail of a sailboat operates like a wing of an airplane. Specifically, the sail is curved so that the path for air going around the outside of the sail is longer than the path on the inside of the sail. Therefore, the air moving along the longer path must move faster than the air on the inside path in order to try to keep up with the overall flow of air past the sail.

As discussed above, the faster-moving air will, according to Bernoulli's principle, have reduced pressure, and this will provide a pull on the outside of the sail. The basic pattern of airflow is shown in Figure 3.1. A sail on a sailboat looks and acts much like the wings on the original Wright brothers' airplanes. Those wings were not solid wings like those found on modern aircraft, but were made of cloth stretched over a frame so as to have a curved profile.

A wing or sail must present some angle to the oncoming flow of air in order to work best. As discussed for keels, this is known as the "angle of attack" and is illustrated in Figure 3.1, which shows

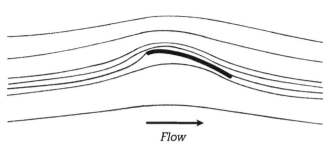

Flow

Fig. 3.1 Air flow around a single sail.

the air flow around a single sail. The flow lines clearly indicate that the paths above the sail are longer than those below it. The general pressure of the flowing air will then cause the air to move faster along the longer paths, and this will produce a decrease in pressure and a pull, or lift, on the sail.

The net force on the sail is actually a combination of the pressure of the wind on the inside of the sail and the suction from the lower pressure along the outside of the sail. Using a barometer carefully fitted by means of a flexible tube to actually measure the pressure at various points on both sides of a sail yields results like those shown in Figure 3.2. Note that the suction on the outside of the sail actually provides a greater force than does the pressure on the inside of the sail. Exactly what these pressure curves look like depends on the specific shape of the sail, the angle of attack into the wind and the speed of the wind. However, the results shown in Figure 3.2 are typical in that the pressure obtained from the suction on the lee-ward side of the sail, as explained by Bernoulli's principle, is three or four times greater than the direct pressure of the wind on the windward side.

Main-Sail Pressure

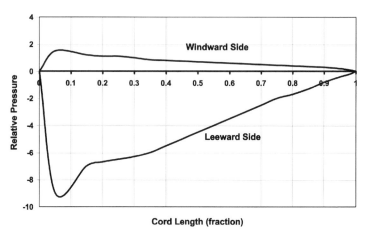

Figure 3.2. The distribution of pressure along both sides of a single (main) sail (adapted from *Yacht Design*, by Larsson and Eliasson). The negative pressure shown for the leeward side is the suction provided by the fast moving air along the outside of the sail as explained by Bernoulli's principle. The positive pressure along the windward side is the direct pressure of the wind on that side. Both of these pressures contribute to the overall force of the sail; the net force on the sail is proportional to the total area between the two curves.

On occasion you may encounter a discussion of sail theory that indicates that the way a sail or airplane wing actually works can be understood completely in terms of the impact of the air molecules on the inside of the sail or wing. These models claim that you only need Newtonian mechanics, i.e., the mathematics of Sir Isaac Newton, to describe the way a sail works and that Bernoulli's principle is not required. However, although air molecules striking the windward side of the sail *do* produce a pressure on that side of the sail, these discussions ignore the fact that air is actually a fluid with forces between the molecules themselves, i.e. the Van der Waals forces discussed earlier.

Because these forces exist, it is possible for air to pull on the sail or wing in areas of reduced pressure and not just act like a bunch of molecular bullets that interact only by collisions with the sail and each other. In any event, Figure 3.2 clearly shows that it is the combination of both high pressure on the windward part of the sail and reduced pressure on the leeward part of the sail that provides the total force on the sail. As seen in Figure 3.1, the suction on the leeward side provides more than two-thirds of the overall force on the sail, and this is typical.

The net force on the sail is not in the direction of motion of the boat, except for the case of sailing directly downwind. Usually the wind is coming at the boat at an angle somewhere between about 30 degrees and 180 degrees with respect to the direction of motion. Since in general the wind is coming from abeam or even forward of abeam, the force exerted on the sail will have a direction that points at some angle to the motion of the boat.

Exactly what this angle is depends on the direction of the wind with respect to the direction of motion of the boat as well as the angle of the sail with respect to the centerline of the boat. A typical situation is shown in Figure 3.3. (This figure was presented also in Chapter 2.)

Because it is at an angle, the net force from the wind in the sail can be broken up or "resolved" into

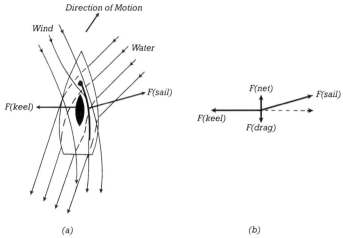

Figure 3.3. Balance between lift from air flow around the sail and water flow around the keel for a boat moving about 30° away from the wind direction. Part (a) shows the effect of the wind past the sail and the water flowing around the keel; part (b) shows the force vectors (arrows) and how they combine. The dashed arrow is the component of the force on the sail that just balances the force on the keel. The upward arrow is the net force from the sail and keel combined. The downward arrow in (b) is the drag, or resistance, of the boat as it moves through the water. At constant speed, all these forces just balance each other.

one component along the direction of motion of the boat and one component perpendicular to the motion of the boat. It is the component in the direction of motion that actually propels the boat along its path, of course.

The other component is trying to move the boat sideways, and it is this component that must be balanced by the lift provided by the flow of water past the keel. As long as the wind is steady and the helm is maintained in one direction, an equilibrium will be obtained between the sideways forces from the sail and the keel that balance each other and the boat will be propelled forward by the other component of the force of the wind on the sail.

Of course, the resistance of the hull and keel through the water provides a force in the backward direction, and the forward component of the force on the sails needs to be greater than this force if the boat is to accelerate or equal to this force in order to keep the boat moving forward at a constant speed. If the forward force is less than the backward force the boat will either stop or slow down to where the backward force is equal to the forward force, at which point the boat will once again move forward at a constant speed.

As discussed earlier with regards to how the keel works, and as shown once again in Figure 3.3, the boat does not move directly along the direction of the long axis of the boat, but rather at a bit of an angle. It is this "sidling" that provides the angle of attack for the keel in its motion through the water so that it will generate the necessary lift. Of course, these two forces do not *have* to balance each other out. For example, if you try to sail too close to the wind, or you don't put the sail at the correct angle, it is possible that the sideways force from the sail will be greater than the lifting force from the keel, in which case the boat will drift sideways. A good sailor always tries to avoid this by changing his heading or the sheeting angle of the sail so that his boat will sail without making too much leeway.

Naturally, this is another area in which a sailor needs to find some kind of a compromise, balancing the advantages against the disadvantages of different kinds of sail trim. If, for example, you orient the sail at an angle that is more perpendicular to the wind, the angle of attack will be greater and you can generate more lift, but this will produce a larger component in the sideways direction and a smaller component in the direction of travel.

If, on the other hand, you place the sail at a direction less into the wind, there will be less lift and a net smaller force on the sail, even though the component in the forward direction will be a larger fraction of the total force. Generally, some angle in between will be optimum.

Not surprisingly, this all becomes quite complicated since you must also consider the resistance produced by the induced vortices behind the sail, boat and keel, and how these vary with changes in wind and hull speed. Ultimately, a good sailor will try a number of different angles for the sail and either watch the knotmeter or just "feel" for the best speed in the desired direction of motion. Although we are trying to present the science of sailing here, it is a pursuit like most others that ultimately becomes an art as well as a science.

3.2 Induced Drag

Just as with the water flowing past the hulls and keels, vortices are generated by the wind flowing past the sails. As discussed above, the wind flow produces a higher pressure on the inside and a lower pressure on the outside of the sails. And just as with the water flowing along a keel, this produces a net flow of air over the top of the sail, from the high pressure side to the low pressure side. (See the discussion and Figure 2.7 illustrating this for a keel in Chapter 2.)

Because the wind is flowing primarily toward the stern, these upward and downward flows meet at the back of the sail at angles with respect to each other and produce a twisting effect on the flow of air off the sail that becomes more pronounced as you move up the sail.

Furthermore, if a sail has much of a gap between the deck of the boat and the bottom of the sail, a vortex can be generated there as well. These

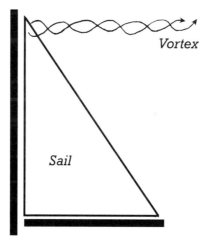

Figure 3.4. Schematic representation of vortex formation at the top of a sail.

Figure 3.5. Vortices formed at the top of sails observed in low-lying fog by the boats in the 2001-2002 Volvo Ocean Race as they left Cape Town, South Africa. (*Photo by Daniel Forster, with permission*).

vortices are shown schematically in Figure 3.4. The production of these vortices requires energy, and this energy must come from the wind power in the sail. An example of these vortices produced at the top of a sail is shown in Figure 3.5, which shows boats from the 2001-2002 Volvo Ocean Race proceeding through a fog just after leaving Cape Town, South Africa. The induced vortices are seen clearly in the fog and indicate that a considerable amount of energy has been dissipated this way.

Just as for a keel, you can use wing theory in order to try to design the most efficient sail shape. As discussed for keels, the most efficient shape for minimizing vortices is a tall, narrow sail, although as we will see, such a shape is not the most optimum for downwind sailing and is often not practical. Ultimately, as was the case with keels, the best shape is one that provides an elliptical distribution of lift along the sail. However, this shape is generally not very practical for mainsails, in particular, since you need to take advantage of the space behind the mast and in front of the backstay, which is why you generally see triangular sails.

Recently, it has become common, especially on racing boats, to see mainsail shapes that are more elliptical at the top in order to try to reduce the effects of induced drag vortices behind the mainsail. But this shape requires changes in the geometry of the backstay rigging and/or a willingness of the crew to "help" the mainsail move from one side to the other on tacks and jibes. Otherwise, this extra curvature or "roach" on the trailing edge of the main tends to get hung up on a fixed backstay, especially in light air.

3.3 Turbulence

Wind moving along a sail will generally produce turbulence in the air, just as water produces turbulence flowing along a hull. The origin of this turbulence is the shearing of the wind due to the motion of the boat through the air. As was the case with water flowing along the hull, the air molecules immediately on the surface of the sail are attached by small intermolecular forces to the surface of the sail, and these molecules move with the sail. A few feet out from the sail, however, the air molecules are moving with the general motion of the air in the atmosphere, often in the opposite direction of the sail, which causes the air to be sheared. This shearing requires energy and is the source of the friction of the sail through the air. The shearing process also introduces sideways components in the motion of the air that lead to the formation of turbulence. As soon as turbulence is formed, the friction increases considerably.

We can use the discussion presented in Chapter 1 regarding Reynold's number to estimate how far along a sail you can expect the air flow to change from being laminar, or smooth, to turbulent. Recall that the Reynold's number is given by

$$R = (L\ v) / (\mu / \rho),$$

where, for this application, L is the length along the sail, v is the velocity of the air past the sail, μ is the viscosity of air and ρ is the density of air. As discussed earlier for the case of water flowing past the hull, what Reynolds found was that in general, for any fluid, including air or water, turbulence will begin when the Reynold's number is equal to about one million (10^6). The viscosity of air is much less than the viscosity of water, i.e., it is easier to shear, but so is its density, so that the ratios are comparable. The viscosity of air has been measured to be $\mu = 1.8 \times 10^{-5}$ N • sec / m^2, and the density is 1.2 kg / m^3. Hence the Reynold's number is

$$R = (L \, v) \, / \, (\, 1.5 \times 10^{-5} \; m^2/sec), \; or$$

$$R = (L \, v) \; (\, 0.67 \times 10^5 \,),$$

with L in m and v in m/sec. As discussed in Chapter 1, when this number is about 10^6, turbulence will occur. For a typical wind speed of 10 knots or 5 m/sec, this will occur for $L = 3$ m, or about 10 feet. Hence, you can expect that turbulence will begin somewhere along the sail. For higher wind speeds, it will move up closer to the luff of the sail, and for lower wind speeds you may actually have laminar flow all the way along the sail. In general, turbulence will occur, and you must expect that there will be an increase in the resistance of the sail moving through the air because of it.

The turbulence discussed here is not to be confused with eddies that can be formed behind a sail due to so-called "separation." In this case, if the angle of attack of the sail into the wind is too great, the wind will not be able to continue smoothly along the curvature of the sail all the way to the back of the sail, and the flow of air will leave the surface of the sail and proceed more directly to the rear. This separation will leave a partial vacuum along the back part of the sail, and air will move into this vacuum creating eddies as it does. This effect, as well as that of laminar flow and turbulence formation, is shown in the drawing of Figure 3.6.

The result of separation is to reduce the efficiency of the sail in two ways: First, it effectively shortens the sail since the sail is most efficient only along the path to the separation point and lift can only be obtained along this part very effectively. Second, the creation of eddies takes energy, which again must come from the wind power in the sail.

Most sailors know that separation is not a good thing and watch for indications that the wind is not flowing along the sail all the way to the rear. These indications include the flapping of the rear part of the sail (the leech) and the flapping of "telltales" attached to the sail. Telltales are small streamers, typically about three inches long, that are attached to the sail just behind the luff or on the leech. These can be very helpful in checking for smooth flow along the sail. If the separation occurs very close to the luff of the sail, the sail may "stall" and lose nearly all power. Every sailor has managed to be in this situation from time to time. In order to get the maximum power available from a sail, you want to have smooth, attached flow as far along the sail as possible.

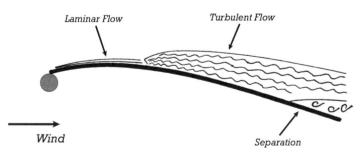

Figure 3.6. Air flow along a sail, showing laminar flow, turbulence formation, and separation.

3.4 Sail Interaction

Most sailboats use two or more sails simultaneously. The most common type of cruising sailboat is the sloop, which has a single mast with two sails, one in front of the mast and one behind the mast.

The front sail may be either a jib or a genoa jib, with the latter just being a somewhat oversized jib. A jib fills the area from the headstay to the mast, while a genoa, or "genny," extends beyond the mast and begins to overlap the sail behind it with a number designation describing how far this overlap goes. For example, if the genoa extends beyond the mast by a distance equal to 35 percent of the distance between the mast and the bottom of the forestay, it is called a 135 genoa. (Most genoas range in size from 110 to 150%.)

Of course, the sail mounted behind the mast is called the mainsail and is normally attached along its luff directly to the mast with its bottom edge or "foot" attached to the boom. Some cruising sailboats carry a small third sail on another mast at the rear of the boat making the boat a "ketch" if the mast for the third sail is in front of the rudder post or a "yawl" if this mast is behind the rudder post. Less common, but seen every so often, are large sailboats with two large masts of roughly equal height or with a rear mast that is actually taller than the front mast, in which case the boat is called a schooner.

In any event, most sailboats have more than one sail, and some have three or more. We wish to

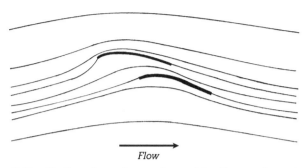

Figure 3.7. Air flow for a two-sail combination as found on a typical sloop.

discuss briefly here how having more than one sail affects how sails work. We will consider the most common case of the sloop, with one mast and two sails, as our example.

In Figure 3.7 the diagram shows the air flow patterns around two sails together as they would commonly be on a sloop. Note that there is a net larger displacement of the air perpendicular to the general direction of flow for the two-sail case when compared to a single sail as shown in Figure 3.1. This is because the two sails act to create, in effect, a larger wing around which the air must move. The total path around the outside is also longer, and the differential in air speeds on the leeward and windward sides is greater with two sails, which helps to create even more lift.

For some time, this effect was believed to be due to something referred to as the "slot effect," with the gap between the two sails supposedly funneling more air at a higher speed along the outer surface of the mainsail, thus causing the mainsail to produce more lift. Since then, however, measurements of the actual lift along both sails have shown that this is really not the case. Rather it is the fact that the combination essentially produces a single larger airfoil that creates greater total lift. Note that it is normally true that it will be the foresail, not the main, that produces the greater part of the total lift. In fact, even if you use only a fairly small foresail, you will find that the total lift is significantly increased.

Figure 3.8 shows some measurements of the lift and pressure for an individual jib and mainsail compared to the two-sail combination. As was the case with Figure 3.2, the positive pressure on the windward side comes from the direct interaction of the wind with the sail, and the negative pressures indicated for the leeward side represent suction due to the faster-moving air on that side and Bernoulli's principle. It is readily apparent that the front sail, i.e., the genoa, experiences a great increase in lift with the two-sail combination and that while the mainsail experiences a net loss of lift, the total lift is greater than what you could obtain with either sail alone. True, it is not as great as it would be from two completely separate sails of the same sizes. But given the fact that most sailors prefer to use only one mast, the combination can achieve a reasonable fraction, i.e., two-thirds to three-quarters of the amount you would obtain from the sum of two completely independent sails.

Up to this point the discussion has ignored the effect of the mast and the fact that it can both

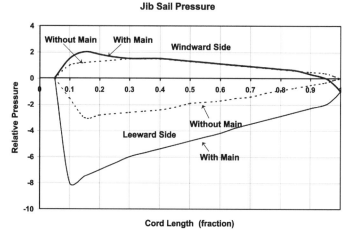

Figure 3.8.a. The relative pressures on a genoa sail with and without a mainsail also present. (Adapted from *Yacht Design*, by Larsson and Eliasson.) This figure is similar to Fig. 3.2; the positive pressures shown for the windward side represent the direct effect of the wind on that side of the sail and the negative pressures indicated for the leeward side indicate the suction on that side due to the fast moving air there as explained by Bernoulli's principle. The presence of the mainsail greatly increases the power of the genoa, especially on the leeward (downwind) side.

produce turbulence and cause separation at the luff of the mainsail. Usually the flow will reattach as it moves along the sail, but still some power is lost. Fortunately, as an added benefit of using two sails in combination, an overlapping genoa can often reduce the negative effect of the mast by maintaining the flow through the slot with less turbulence. The net result is that the modern combination of a genoa and mainsail can be a very efficient combination to obtain power from a single mast.

Main-Sail Pressure

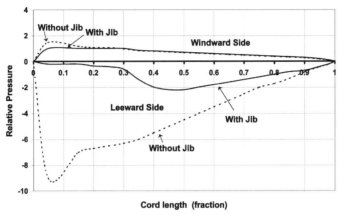

Figure 3.8.b. The relative pressures on a mainsail with and without a genoa sail also present. (Adapted from *Yacht Design*, by Larsson and Eliasson.) The positive pressures shown for the windward side represent the direct effect of the wind on that side of the sail and the negative pressures indicated for the leeward side indicate the suction on that side due to the fast moving air there as explained by Bernoulli's principle. The presence of the genoa sail significantly decreases the power of the mainsail.

It is important, of course, to get the spacing between the sails correct along with a balance between the sail areas in order to obtain the most efficient overall use of sail area. Unfortunately, the correct solution to these problems varies with wind speed, angle into the wind and boat geometry, so that as with all other things having to do with sailboats, a compromise must be struck for best overall performance. Of course, if you are willing to change your sails for different conditions, you can come closer to having the correct combination all the time.

With this in mind, race teams often do extensive computer modeling, wind tunnel tests and trial runs in order to determine the best geometry for various kinds of sail combinations in various kinds of conditions. Competitors in the 2001-2002 Volvo Ocean Race, for example, carried 19 different sails in order to have the optimum combination in place at all times. Let us consider next the types of sails that are best for sailing downwind versus reaching versus upwind sailing.

3.5 Sail Shapes for Different Points of Sail

It is fairly well known that a fuller or "squareish" sail is best for downwind sailing and that a tall, more triangular sail is better for upwind sailing. With what we have already discussed, it is now possible to understand why this is so.

First of all, let us consider downwind sailing. This is the point of sail that is most obviously workable, especially to nonsailors. If you go out on the water in any kind of boat and place a large sail up into the wind, the wind in the sail will start to move the boat downwind in a natural way. Furthermore, if you wish to go faster, it is clear that more sail will help.

This kind of sail has been used on all kinds of sailing vessels, since before recorded history began. The Vikings' "long boats" had this kind of sail, as did many boats used by the early civilizations of the

Middle East and Far East. Probably native people all over the globe have used such sails at one time or another.

You don't have to go sailing for very long, however, before it becomes clear that downwind isn't the only direction that you might like to go, and that if you wish to sail perpendicular to the direction of the wind, you need to be able to rotate the sail around the mast so that it is no longer parallel to the wind direction on this new angle of sail. People quickly figured this out and, as discussed above, learned that for such sailing, the best solution is to set the sail at approximately a 45-degree angle to both the axis of the boat and the wind direction. So far, so good.

Unfortunately even sailing perpendicular to the wind direction is not always good enough. So sailors began to try to sail "into the wind," and as they did so, they discovered that the good-old square sail was not the most efficient shape. Triangular sails were developed for such use and such sails were seen on ancient Egyptian and other Middle Eastern boats even thousands of years ago. Probably, these people did not understand why the triangular shape worked better upwind, but they learned from experience that it did. We can now understand why this is so.

Before we do this, however, let us first discuss why downwind sailing is not actually the *fastest* point of sail, something that most sailors know very well, but which comes as a bit of a surprise to most nonsailors. The reason is that when you sail directly downwind, the fastest you can hope to go is the speed of the wind. (And of course, you can never go even that fast since there is always some resistance due to the motion through the water.) As boat speed comes up to the wind speed, the force of the wind in the sails reduces, i.e., as the sails are moving with the wind and the difference between the two becomes less and less, there is less and less pressure on the sails to provide greater speed.

Now consider sailing on a beam reach, i.e., perpendicular to the wind direction, with the sail set at approximately a 45-degree angle with respect to the boat and the wind for maximum efficiency. This time, no matter how fast the boat is moving, the wind is still striking the sail from abeam with the same speed and force. This is because the direction of motion is perpendicular to the wind direction, and the boat is no longer sailing "away" from the wind. In other words, it does not matter how fast the boat is moving, the driving force remains constant.

Of course, resistance grows with speed through the water; hence an equilibrium will be reached where the driving force just equals the resistive force and the boat speed remains constant. But if you can reduce the resistive force, the speed can increase quite dramatically. Perhaps the best example of this is seen in iceboat sailing. For these craft, the resistance can be made to be quite small, and the top speeds are amazing. Ice boats routinely can go more than 60 mph while moving on a beam reach in a 20 mph wind! Speeds up to 150 mph have been recorded with wind speeds less than 30 mph.

This sort of performance can also be achieved by multihull sailboats equipped with hydrofoils that lift the boat out of the water at higher speeds. Such boats are not limited by the hull speed applicable to displacement boats, and as a result they are able to obtain speeds of greater than 40 knots with wind speeds of 20 knots.

The same result holds for ordinary sailboats, although the resistance is much greater and the top speeds are much less. The fastest point of sail for most sailboats is at an angle of slightly more than 90 degrees away from the direction of the wind. If you steer a more upwind course, the component of the force of the wind on the sails that is in the direction of motion begins to fall off. If you head more downwind, the speed of the boat begins to subtract from the wind speed for the net wind speed in the sails.

In Figure 3.9 we show a typical "polar plot" of the speed of a sailboat as a function of the direction of motion relative to the wind direction. Note that the boat is fastest at an angle of about 100 degrees away from the wind. Even without polar plots, sailors usually learn this by experience fairly quickly. Often you will find that if you want to travel directly downwind, it is actually quicker to sail a little off course onto a broad reach and jibe back and forth toward your destination. This makes the distance traveled a bit greater, but the overall time of travel may actually be less. Of course, it is also clear in Figure 3.9 that the boat actually cannot point closer than about 30 degrees off the wind, and that the

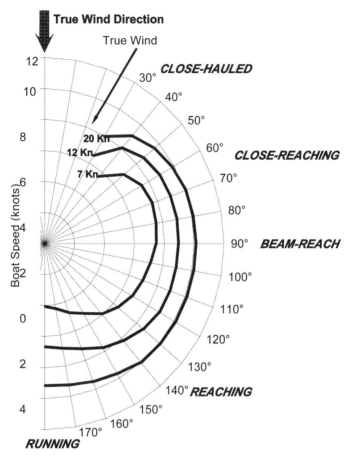

Figure 3.9 A "polar plot" showing the speed of a typical sail-boat as a function of the angle of sail away from the wind direction, for three different wind speeds. For the lighter wind of 7 knots, the fastest point of sail is actually slightly forward of 90° away from the wind direction; as the wind speed increases, the fastest point of sail moves backward to somewhat downwind of 90°. (Adapted from *Aero-Hydrodynamics of Sailing,* by C. A. Marchaj.)

boat speed will suddenly drop off as you come around to try to point directly into the wind.

Perhaps this is a good place to discuss *apparent wind* since it is closely related to the effects of wind direction on course and speed. Specifically, the wind that you experience as a boat is moving through the water is actually a combination of the "true" direction of the wind over the water and the air movement that is the result of the motion of the boat. The latter wind, for example, could be felt in a power boat moving through the water on a day with no wind at all. It is also the wind you feel when riding in a car and sticking your hand out the window. Because this wind, due to the motion of the boat, will always come from in front, the combination of this wind with the true wind over the water will always be more from the front of the boat than the direction of the true wind alone.

In the case of the iceboat example above, the rider will feel a wind of 60 mph from the front direction due to the motion of the iceboat combined with the 20 mph true wind from the side. The net wind felt will be the vector combination of these two winds and will be a 63 mph wind coming from 18 degrees away from directly ahead. For the case of a sailboat moving at 5 knots with a 10-knot wind from the side, the effect is not so dramatic, and would produce an apparent wind of 11 knots coming from 26 degrees forward of abeam (or 64 degrees off directly ahead).

The reason that apparent wind is important to understand is that it is the only wind that you actually experience on the boat! This includes any wind vane mounted on the mast, bits of yarn streaming from the shrouds or smoke coming from a pipe. Often, when moving as close to the wind direction as possible, it actually feels like the wind is coming from directly ahead. But, of course, this is not the case since even the apparent wind must be from the side a little bit, and the true wind is usually at least 30 degrees or more away from the bow. Anyway, let us now consider in more detail, what is happening in upwind sailing.

Most recreational and cruising sailboats can sail to about 45 degrees off the direction of the wind. By designing the boat and the sails especially for upwind sailing, it is possible to sail to within 30 degrees of the wind direction in ideal conditions. How is this possible? And what can you do to improve the ability of a boat to go to windward? The simple answer is that you must have a very efficient keel and use tall, narrow sails. Let us discuss these points briefly.

When you are sailing to windward, the forward component of the force of the wind on the sails becomes relatively small and the sideways component becomes large. Therefore, if the keel cannot generate enough lift, i.e., enough sideways force in the opposite direction to the sideways force from the wind in the sails, then the boat will drift sideways and begin to fall off from the desired direction into the wind.

For this purpose, you want a keel that can generate good lift with minimal induced drag, i.e., vortices. As discussed above, the keel design that best does both of these things best is a deep, narrow keel, and this is what you will find on modern racing yachts, such as for the entrants in the 2001-2002 Volvo Around the World Race. Of course, you can not always use a deep keel, especially if you are interested in entering shallow bays or anchorages, so a compromise is usually necessary. The most popular choice for an efficient keel with minimum drag and induced resistance on cruising sailboats at this time is a tapered keel around four or five feet deep with a bulb and wings at the bottom to help reduce induced drag vortices and increase righting moment to keep the boat from heeling too much. Figure 2.11, which showed the keel for a 2003 cruising sailboat, was an example of this.

The other major consideration for sailing upwind is the *shape* of the sails. When sailing downwind, there is relatively little wind flowing past the sails, so vortex generation is minimal and your main concern is to project as much sail area as possible. When you are pointing into the wind, however, the relative velocity of the wind past the sails increases, and this increased velocity of the wind causes the induced resistance to increase significantly, i.e., the vortices off the leech of the sail grow considerably. Hence you want to use a sail that produces more lift with less induced drag, which, as was the case for the keel, requires a taller, narrower geometry. So for downwind sailing, you use a more "square," sail to catch as much of the wind as possible. But as you come around and point more into the wind, then you need to worry more and more about the induced drag, which means you will want a sail with a higher aspect ratio, i.e., taller and narrower.

The relative merits of the different sail shapes are shown for a particular boat in Figure 3.10. This figure shows the driving force for three different sails, all with the same total area, but different aspect ratios, as a function of the angle of sail away from the wind direction. It's immediately apparent that at angles of sail close to the wind direction, none of the sails is able to obtain nearly as much driving force as it can for an angle of around 90 degrees. However, the sail with an aspect ratio of 3:1, i.e., a sail that is about three times as tall as its

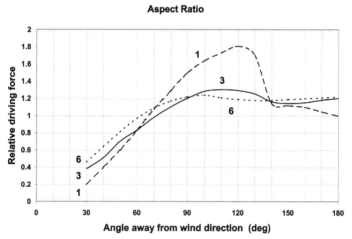

Figure 3.10 The relative driving force as a function of direction of sail away from the wind direction for three different sails, with aspect ratios of 1, 3, and 6 respectively, as indicated. (Adapted from *Yacht Design*, by Larsson and Eliasson.)

average width, is able to obtain a driving force nearly two times that of the square sail with an aspect ratio of 1:1. The sail with an aspect ratio of 6:1 does even better. As the point of sail comes around to a beam reach and finally to a run, the sail with the lower aspect ratio becomes increasingly efficient.

You can see these principles clearly in use on modern racing sailboats, as shown for entrants in the 2003 America's Cup race in Figures 3.11 and 3.12. When pointing upwind, racers use tall, narrow sails, with elliptical-shaped leeches near the top. When pointing downwind, they get out the spinnaker, which is a very broad sail that provides a large area for catching the wind. Modern racers in the high-profile events with corporate support will often have more than a dozen sails on board at once in order to have just the right size and shape sails up all the time. Clearly, a recreational cruising sailor has neither the money nor the manpower to handle so many sails. Still it can help to have a few different genoas and a good spinnaker or two.

3.6 Sail Trim

Now that we have a general understanding of how sails work and why you use different sails for different points of sail, we can understand why you trim sails differently for different points of sail and even for the same point of sail, depending on wind speed

Figure 3.11 The winner of the 2003 America's Cup race, ALINGHI, moving into the wind. Note the tall sails with high aspect ratio and the elliptical shape on the top of the mainsail. *(Photo by Rick Tomlinson, with permission.)*

Figure 3.12 The yachts Alinghi and Team New Zealand moving downwind in the 2003 America's Cup race. Note the low aspect ratios of the asymmetrical spinnakers used for optimum downwind sailing. *(Photo by Rick Tomlinson, with permission.)*

and boat speed. Note that a "point" of sail refers to the direction one is sailing with respect to the wind direction.

As indicated in Figure 3.9 above, when proceeding directly downwind, one is said to be "running." If the wind is from the side, one is "reaching." If the wind is from behind, but not directly behind, it is a "broad" reach. If the wind is straight from the side, or abeam, it is a "beam" reach. If the wind is somewhat forward of sideways, one is on a "close" reach. Finally, if one is sailing as close to straight into the wind as possible (usually this is about 45 degrees away from the wind direction), one is said to be "close hauled."

As discussed in the previous section, as you go from running to reaching to close hauled, you will find that the most efficient sail shape changes from a broad sail to a tall, narrower sail. However, it is not just the basic dimensions of sail shape that change, but also how you trim the sail. "Trimming" the sail is concerned with how flat or curvaceous you make a given sail, and also the angle of the sail with respect to the boat and the wind. Of course, there are entire books on how to trim sails for best performance including *The New Book of SAIL Trim,* edited by Ken Textor. It is not our purpose here to go through how to trim sails for all possible conditions and for all different sorts of sails and boats, but rather to consider the basics of sail trim and to try to understand *why* you trim sails differently for different conditions.

First of all, most sailors know that as you go from pointing downwind to pointing upwind, it is necessary to angle the sails in closer to the centerline of the boat. As discussed above, a sail works by a combination of the wind pushing on the windward side and pulling on the leeward side.

For downwind sailing, if you placed the angle of the sail parallel to the centerline of the boat, it would also be parallel to the wind direction and the wind would just rush along both sides producing no pressure or suction at all. If, on the other hand, you placed the sail at some intermediate angle, say around 45 degrees to the angle of the wind, then there would be both pressure and lift, and the resultant force from the sail would be at some angle to the desired direction of travel and the boat would start to sidle off in that direction.

Obviously, if you wish to go straight downwind, then it is best to place the sail so that it is essentially perpendicular to the centerline of the boat. That way the wind will fill the sail, and the boat will move in the desired direction. In fact, when sailing in this direction, you really have almost no choice but to place the sail in this orientation. For the most part the wind will just produce pressure on the windward side, although there will still be some circulation around the sail, and a small amount of suction on the leeward side. Usually it is also best to ease the various control lines like the outhaul, halyard and sheets so as to produce a rounded, or bulbous shape for the sail. This shape helps to catch the wind better and provides more help for obtaining suction on the leeward side from Bernoulli's principle.

Note that the relative wind speed past the sail will be small. The boat is moving downwind and the net speed of the wind, i.e., the apparent wind, in the sail is the difference between the true wind speed and the speed of the boat. On the plus side, at this small relative wind speed, the air flow is able to stay attached farther along a relatively highly curved sail.

Consider now moving along a beam reach with the wind from the side. As discussed earlier, you will need to orient the sail at an angle of approximately 45 degrees with respect to the centerline of the boat in order to provide the necessary net force to propel the boat forward. You will now find it necessary to also flatten the sail somewhat from the shape used for downwind sailing. The amount of flattening will depend on the wind speed, with higher wind speeds requiring more flattening. The reason for this is that there is now a higher apparent wind speed flowing along the sail, and if the sail is too curved, the wind cannot stay attached all the way to the leech of the sail. You often have to determine the exact sheeting angle and the shape of the sail by trial and error for a given point of sail and wind speed. Experience helps a lot.

Finally consider a boat that is close-hauled, sailing as far into the wind direction as possible. The sail angle now must be almost parallel to the centerline of the boat or else the net force from the sail will be backwards. The sideways component of the sail force is a bigger fraction of the total sail force, and ultimately you cannot point any closer to the direction the wind is coming from because you cannot continue to obtain a net force that points forward at all. The apparent wind speed is now at maximum, and the speed of the wind along the sail is great; hence the sail must now be very flat in order to prevent separation almost immediately near the front of the sail. Again, the exact sail angle and the flattening required need to be different for different wind speeds and are determined by trying different settings.

So we see that the general rule is that the angle of the sail moves from perpendicular to the centerline of the boat to nearly parallel as you go from pointing downwind to pointing upwind. We also see that the sail will need to be flatter as you point more upwind in order to prevent separation.

Note that sail trim needs to change as the wind speed changes, even as you continue along the same point of sail. Specifically, as the wind increases, you need to flatten the sails in order to prevent separation and maintain power. If the wind slackens, you usually will want to ease the sheets controlling the shape of the sail so that they become fuller, i.e., more rounded in shape. This provides more power and will work because separation moves farther back on the sail as wind speed decreases.

Finally, sailors who race generally know that if you want to *accelerate* fastest, whether in response to a sudden increase in wind speed or after tacking, it helps to start with the sail relatively curved and flatten it as the boat speed increases. This really is like shifting a car up through its gears as it goes faster. The fuller sail for the low boat speed allows the sail to catch the wind more effectively and will provide more lift by Bernoulli's principle, thus providing more power to accelerate the boat. As the boat moves faster, in a general upwind direction, the apparent wind speed increases and it becomes impossible to prevent separation as the wind moves back along the sail.

The flattening process should generally be done fairly quickly; usually within a minute or less after tacking and starting on a new direction. If the flattening is in response to an increase in wind speed, it may be done more slowly, following the increasing wind speed. This flattening with increasing boat speed is something that competitive racers need to use to compete effectively. It often determines who wins a "tacking duel." For more detail on sail trim, *How to Trim Sails* by Peter Schweer is a very useful book.

4

The Physics of Weather for Sailors

As long as we are discussing the physics of sailing, it is appropriate to discuss some of the physics behind the weather as well. We will start by discussing the general physics of local weather, which is what sailors are usually most interested in. Then we will proceed to discuss the physics of global weather patterns. After that we will finish with a brief discussion of global current and tide patterns. These are all of interest to sailors and can be understood with a modest amount of physics.

4.1 Local Weather

Weather is what is happening in the earth's atmosphere. This includes temperatures, winds and precipitation. All of these things are determined by the heating of the earth and its atmosphere by the sun, together with the spinning of the earth. Specifically, the heating of the earth by the sun is not the same all over the earth, and this causes the air to move.

Regions that experience more heating than others will produce rising air masses, with air moving in from the surrounding area along the surface of the earth to replace the rising air. This moving air is deflected to the right in the northern hemisphere and to the left in the southern hemisphere. Scientists say that this deflection is due to the *Coriolis force*, which is caused by the spinning of the earth. Different regions experience different amounts of heating from the sun for two reasons: One is that the region may consist mostly of material that is more or less efficient at absorbing the sunlight that falls on it; the other is that different amounts of sunlight fall on different regions of the earth. Let us consider these two points in somewhat more detail.

First, let's look at the fact that different materials absorb sunlight differently. Black surfaces, for example, absorb most of the sunlight that falls on them, while white materials reflect more sunlight. Everyone knows from experience that a black, tar parking lot gets a lot hotter than the other areas around it on a sunny day. Cities, in general, absorb more sunlight than rural areas and will usually be hotter on sunny days than the countryside because the materials that make up the city's surfaces are more efficient at absorbing sunlight than green grass and farm fields. Along these same lines, land, in general, is more efficient at absorbing sunlight than is water, which causes land to heat up more than water, as long as sunlight is falling on it.

Now, it is a general principle that whatever is a good absorber of radiant energy like sunlight is also a good emitter. Therefore, as long as the sunlight is falling on the good absorber, it absorbs more than it will re-emit. But as soon as the sunlight goes away, i.e., as soon the sun sets, the good absorber will re-emit more than the poor absorber. Hence the land will emit more during the night than water will. The radiation that is re-emitted is not visible light, of course, (one does not see the land emitting light during the night), but is long-wavelength radiation, generally in the infrared part of the electromagnetic spectrum.

In any event, on nice sunny days in the summer when people are sailing, the land will heat up more than the water during the day and then cool off quicker at night, creating heating differences that cause the air to move. Specifically, the hotter air over the land during midday causes the air to rise, since hot air is less dense than cool air, and this rising warmer air is replaced by the cooler air from over the water flowing horizontally along the surface.

In the middle of the night, this process will reverse itself as the air over the water becomes warmer than that over the land. The two air flows are called "sea breezes" and provide cooling for people on the beach during the day and "shore breezes" for sailors to use. If there is no other source of wind on a hot, summer day, a sailor can usually find at least a gentle shore breeze in the mid to late afternoon.

As the warm air over the land rises, it will cool both because it moves away from the warm surface of the land and because it is less dense at higher elevations so that the molecules can spread out, which cools them in a process called *adiabatic* cooling. Cooling air will often cause any water vapor in it to condense, as can be seen on the surface of a cold glass on a hot, humid summer day. This condensing water vapor will then form into clouds, which is why you will sometimes see clouds build up over land near a large body of water on summer afternoons. The presence of these clouds tells you that the shore breezes are there, which can be an invaluable clue, since again, there are times when these shore breezes are the only wind available for sailing.

The more common kind of wind used for sailing is the wind associated with passing pressure systems, due to the fact that certain parts of the earth receive more sunlight than others, i.e., the regions around the equator receive more radiant energy from the sun than do the regions closer to the poles. This difference in heating causes air to rise at the equator; which in turn causes cooler air from the north and south to flow along the earth's surface to take its place. Again, because of the spinning of the earth, this air moving toward the equator is deflected to the right in the northern hemisphere, and to the left in the southern hemisphere. Because the earth is big enough, the flow along the surface turns west in the northern hemisphere and east in the southern hemisphere before it can move all the way from the polar region to the equator. The flow pattern actually breaks up into three cells in each hemisphere, which will be described more fully below.

Before we do this, however, we need to take a closer look at the *Coriolis effect*. The best way to do this is to imagine a missile fired directly northward from the equator. As you do so, remember that the earth is spinning, quite rapidly actually, as it turns once on its axis per day. In fact, the circumference of the earth around the equator is about 24,000 miles, and since it takes one day, or 24 hours, to turn on its axis once, the surface of the earth at the equator is moving 1,000 mph! Now think about how fast the surface of the earth is moving near the poles. For example, if you straddle the pole, with each foot just one foot out from the exact location of the pole, each foot moves completely around the pole in one day. This circle has a radius of 1 foot and a circumference ($C = 2 \pi r$) of 6.3 feet. So your foot is moving only 6.3 feet in 24 hours, or about 0.26 ft/hr, which is 0.00005 mph! The point of all this is that the land is moving much faster at the equator than it is near the poles as it progresses in an eastward direction.

Now, getting back to the missile that we fired northward from the equator, we see that it is moving not only very fast in a northward direction, but also toward the east at 1,000 mph, since it takes on the motion of the earth when it is fired. At first, since the land is also moving toward the east at 1,000 mph, the missile and land move together in an easterly direction. But as the missile moves farther northward, the land is moving less rapidly toward the east, and the missile will begin to move eastward relative to the land, even though it was fired directly northward. Note that east is toward the right as you move northward.

In this same vein, if you fire a missile southward from some point north of the equator, it will move *less* rapidly toward the east than the land underneath it as it proceeds southward, which means it will move toward the west. West is to the right as you move southward. Therefore, we see that all objects moving north or south over the land in the northern hemisphere will move toward the right as they go, due to the spinning of the earth.

Furthermore, even if an object is not moving directly north or south, the north or south components of the motion will still feel this effect, and the object will be deflected to the right. This deflection, then, is said to be due to the Coriolis force. As we see, it is not really a force like gravity, but rather a way of explaining why objects moving over the surface of the earth are deflected due to the spinning of the earth. This effect applies to everything that moves over the surface of the spinning earth, including moving air, i.e., the wind, and even water.

Now let us consider what happens if we have a high- or low-pressure *area* in the northern hemisphere. Air will respond to different pressure areas by flowing from regions of high pressure to regions of low pressure. If there is a high-pressure area, the air will flow outward from this area, and as it does so the air moving from the high pressure area will be defected to the right, and the overall motion will be an outward flow deflecting to the right as it goes.

This produces a clockwise circulation around the high-pressure area. For a low-pressure area, the flow is inward toward the low-pressure center, again with deflection to the right due to the Coriolis force. This produces a spiraling flow pattern that circulates counter-clockwise, as illustrated in Figure 4.1.

Note that in general, low-pressure areas are better defined, i.e., they have a well developed low-pressure region, and the wind movement near this region can become quite strong. These well-defined low-pressure regions we call storms, and are characterized by strong winds circulating counter-clockwise around the low-pressure center.

Also note that in the southern hemisphere, all of this is reversed. The flow pattern around a low-pressure region is clockwise, still due to the Coriolis force. The whole low-pressure system generally moves toward the east in the mid-latitudes of the northern hemisphere, due to the prevailing westerly winds, with the counter-clockwise circulation pattern remaining well defined.

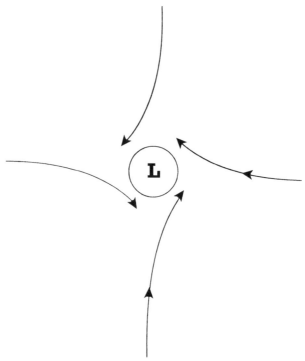

Figure 4.1. Flow pattern of air moving in towards a low pressure area and deflected to the right (the northern hemisphere) by the Coriolis Force. A counterclockwise circulation pattern around the low pressure area develops, as shown.

Knowing these general flow patterns around high- and low-pressure areas enables sailors to understand and even predict what will happen with the weather over the next few hours or days based on the changes that are occurring in the atmosphere.

For example, if you see that the barometer is falling, you know that a low-pressure system is coming. Most people already know that this means a possible storm is approaching. But by noting which way the wind is blowing, you can also get a good idea whether the storm is going to pass directly overhead or go to the north or south. This is because of the fact that close to the low-pressure area, the wind circulates counter-clockwise, so on the east side the wind is from the south, on the north side the wind is from the east, on the west side the wind is from the north and on the south side the wind is from the west.

Thus, if you see that the barometer is falling and the wind is from the south, you not only know that a low-pressure center is approaching, but the center of the low pressure must be directly to the west and will probably pass directly overhead (see Figure 4.1). If, on the other hand, the wind is from the east, then the center of the low is to the south, or if the wind is from the west then the center must be to the north.

These days, with satellite imagery and radar, you can get a much better picture of exactly what is going on by turning on the radio or television. But still it is sometimes not possible to get this information and it helps to have some idea of what must be happening. I certainly recommend using professional weather forecasts and satellite imagery whenever possible for the best weather predicting. But it is always helpful to understand what is happening beyond the simple weather forecasts.

It is not my intention to try to discuss all the intricacies associated with local weather systems; a number of books, including some on sailing, do this in more detail. However, let us discuss one other aspect of local weather as it relates to sailing; namely, the relationship between wind and clouds.

Most sailors know that when a cloud passes overhead, the wind can shift around in very peculiar ways from the normal direction that it has. This is generally due to a strong updraft associated with the cloud. If there are a lot of clouds that are moving into a region, they may have been formed somewhere else and are now being blown with the prevailing winds. But when they first formed, it was from rising, cooling air.

If you are out sailing on a nice, but humid, summer day, and clouds begin to form in the afternoon, as they often do, these clouds are forming where updrafts are occurring. These updrafts may have been caused initially by some local "hot spot" over land or water that warmed the air and started it to rise. But once the updraft starts, it can continue, and as it does, the rising air will cool and begin to condense, eventually forming a cloud.

The important thing, for the sailor, is to realize that there will be an updraft associated with a cloud. As the warm air rises, cooler air will move in along the surface of the water to replace the rising air. But if the system is a small one, for example, if there is just a single cloud, then there might not be enough to set up a counter-clockwise circulation due to the Coriolis force so that the "swirl" around this updraft will unpredictable. In fact, the direction of the swirl will be determined by the combination of the prevailing wind direction and the updraft associated with the cloud.

Fortunately, even though you often cannot predict which way the wind will swirl around a passing cloud, it will probably do it the *same way* for all clouds on the same afternoon. If you can see which way it goes with the first cloud that passes, it will probably do it the same way for other clouds that day. Knowing which way the wind swirls around one passing cloud, you can then try to get to the correct side of the next one in order to get a beneficial wind shift as it goes by.

4.2 Global Weather Patterns

As mentioned above, the weather of the earth is divided up into three cells both to the north and south of the equator—six cells altogether. The existence of these cells was first recognized in the eighteenth century. These cells form bands on the earth similar to those seen on the surface of Jupiter and play a crucial role in determining the global wind and ocean current patterns. It is possible to understand the origin of these bands with just a little physics.

First of all, let us suppose that the earth is not spinning, and that the plane of the equator is the same as the plane of the earth's motion around the sun. (Actually, the earth's axis is tipped at an angle of 23 degrees with respect to the plane of the earth's orbit around the sun.) For this nonrotating, upright earth, the sun's rays would be most perpendicular to the earth's surface at the equator, making

115

it the area where the radiation from the sun would be most intense and the most heating would occur.

It is the *angle* of the sun's rays at the earth's surface that determines where the most heating will occur and not the *distance.* Winter and summer, for example, occur because the earth's axis is tipped, and in the summer the northern hemisphere is tipped toward the sun so that the earth's surface there is more perpendicular to the sun's rays and there is more radiation per unit area than during the winter. In fact, the earth is actually a little closer to the sun during wintertime in the northern hemisphere than it is during summer, but it is this tipping that makes all the difference.

This effect is shown in Figure 4.2. The figure in A shows the situation for sunlight striking the earth at the time of either the autumnal or vernal equinox, i.e., the first day of autumn or the first day of spring. The three bands of rays from the sun have the same cross-sectional area perpendicular to the rays, i.e., these three bands carry the same amount of energy. But the bands that strike the earth nearer to the poles are seen to be spread out over larger surfaces on the earth than is the band that strikes the earth at the equator. For the case shown, the upper and lower bands strike surfaces about 1.5 times as large as the surface that the band at the equator strikes. This means the sunlight is more spread out and will be only about two-thirds as intense as it is near the equator; thus the heating will be correspondingly less away from the equator. This is why it is so much colder at the poles than near the equator. The surface of the earth at the poles is almost parallel to the rays of the sun and a unit surface area receives a much smaller amount of radiation than it does at the equator.

The figure in part B shows the situation near the summer solstice, i.e., the first day of summer. Because the axis of the earth is tipped by 23 degrees with respect to the plane of the orbit of the earth around the sun, at this time the northern hemisphere is tipped toward the sun. The pattern shown in part A is now shifted northward. The middle beam, which strikes the earth perpendicularly, is now above the equator and the upper beam is almost up to the north pole. Therefore the northern hemisphere receives more sunlight in a more perpendicular fashion and hence the intensity of the sunlight is higher. The southern hemisphere, on the other hand, has the sunlight more parallel to its surface, and the energy is more spread out and less intense. This produces summer in the northern hemisphere and winter in the southern hemisphere.

Just the opposite happens for winter in the northern hemisphere. The northern hemisphere is then tipped away from the sun and the southern hemisphere is tipped toward the sun, producing winter in the north and summer in the south.

But let us go back to our simple model of the nonspinning, upright earth. The heating from the sun is always greatest at the equator and least at the poles. Because of the heating of the earth at the equator, the air will warm up there and become less dense and rise, after which this rising air will be

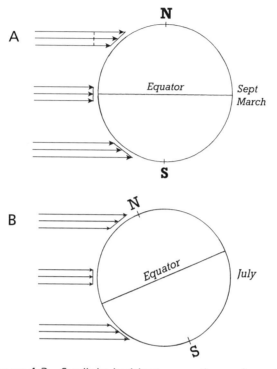

Figure 4.2. Sunlight incident upon the surface of the Earth. Fig. 4.2 (A) shows the situation at the time of the vernal or autumnal equinox. The sunlight is more spread out over the surface of the earth away from the equator; this is what causes it to be warmer near the equator. Fig. 4.2 (B) shows the situation at the time of the summer solstice. Because of the tip of the earth's axis with respect to the plane of its orbit around the sun, the northern hemisphere is now tipped toward the sun and the southern hemisphere away from the sun. This tipping makes the sunlight more concentrated on the surface in the northern hemisphere and more spread out in the southern hemisphere. This produces summer in the northern hemisphere and winter in the southern hemisphere; at the winter solstice, the situation is reversed and the northern hemisphere is tipped away from the sun, producing winter in that hemisphere.

replaced by cooler air moving toward the equator from the polar regions. The rising warmer air will then move toward the poles to replace the air moving south from there along the surface, eventually cooling and sinking in the polar regions. Two giant loops of circulation will therefore form, one in the northern hemisphere and one in the southern hemisphere. This "single cell" model is shown in Figure 4.3.

Of course, in reality the situation is far more complicated because the earth is spinning and the

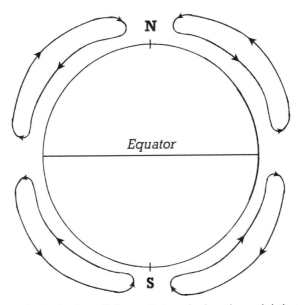

Figure 4.3 A single cell (in each hemisphere) model that one would expect for a non-spinning earth. The warm air at the equator rises and moves towards the poles; the cool air near the poles moves along the surface of the earth toward the equator to replace the rising warmer air.

movement of air is modified by the Coriolis force. In fact, as mentioned earlier, the earth is spinning fast enough, and is large enough, that the air can not make it all the way from the pole to the equator before it is moving directly westward.

Specifically, the air only makes it about one-third of the way, with the result that the one large cell that you would have for a nonspinning earth is broken up into three cells. These cells are shown in Figure. 4.4.

The top and bottom cells have the air moving from the north toward the south along the surface of the earth as it would for the nonspinning case, and the air in the middle cell circulates the other way in order to match up with the flow patterns of these two cells. If the middle cell did not circulate the opposite way, there would exist discontinuities in the air movement that the atmosphere could not support.

The cell just above the equator is called the Hadley cell, after an 18th century geophysicist who first realized that this kind of circulation must exist. The top cell is called the polar cell and the middle one is called the Ferrel cell. These three cells in each hemisphere on the earth are much like the bands observed on Jupiter, although in the case of Jupiter, which is a much larger planet, several bands are actually formed between the poles and the equator. Furthermore, because of the constituents of the atmosphere of Jupiter, there exists coloring that can be observed to be moving with the motion of the bands.

The result for the earth is that bands of air moving east and west are formed along the earth's sur-

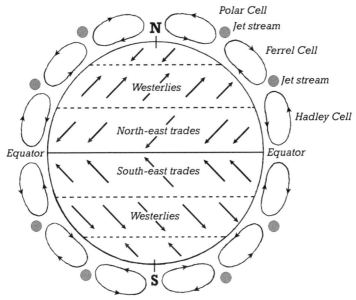

Figure 4.4 The three-cell (in each hemisphere) model of global air circulation observed for the spinning earth. The simple one-cell model of Fig. 4.3 is broken up into three cells by the action of the Coriolis Force created by the spinning of the earth.

face about a third of the way down from the pole and a third of the way up from the equator, as shown in Figure 4.4. This is still a simplified model, of course, because it ignores the fact that there are large land masses on the surface of the earth that heat up and cool down more quickly than do the oceans, as well as the fact that the earth is tipped with respect to its orbit around the sun. Nevertheless, this model describes the generally observed wind patterns of the earth fairly well.

Above the equator are the northeast trade

winds, followed by the boundary between the Hadley and Ferrel cells. Above this boundary are observed the so-called "westerlies" that dominate the region of the middle cell where the continental United States lies. The northeast trades and the westerlies exist because of these cells and the Coriolis force, which deflects the moving air as shown. Similar wind patterns are created in the southern hemisphere. At the equator, the northeast trades meet with southeast trades coming up from the southern hemisphere and form a region with generally very little wind known to sailors as the doldrums.

In the upper atmosphere where these cells meet, you find the so-called "jet streams." These bands of air, at about 30,000 feet, are actually eddies formed in the boundaries between the circulatory cells, as shown in the drawing of Figure 4.4. Because these eddies are located at the boundaries between the cells where the motion is primarily east-west, they also move east-west. Since this occurs at relatively high altitudes there is much less atmosphere (about half as much air to be exact), and the east-west velocity can be rather large.

You will often hear about jet streams on the daily weather programs on TV and radio, and they are often discussed as if they *cause* certain types of weather to prevail. But while these jet streams can sometimes move so-called "high-level" weather systems, in fact, the most significant thing about them is that they are markers that indicate the boundaries between the cells.

Most of the United States, for example, is usually in the middle of the middle cell. Since this is a counter-rotating cell, with air flow from south to north and a deflection to the east caused by the Coriolis force, there is a general flow of air from the southwest, which brings up warm air from the south to the upper regions of the United States during the summer. As winter begins, however, the northern hemisphere is tipped more away from the sun, the loss of heating moves the cell patterns more southward, and the upper part of the United States begins to be closer to the upper cell, the polar cell. In this cell, the general flow of air is from the north toward the south and the upper United States gets lots of cold polar air and suddenly becomes much colder.

The jet stream marks this boundary and when the weather map shows this jet stream to have moved south of where you live, you know that you are now under the influence of the polar cell with its colder air. (Actually, the jet stream is not always directly above the boundary between the cells on the earth's surface, but can be somewhat north or south of the surface boundary.)

Of course, the earth is not entirely covered by oceans. It has large land masses, and as noted earlier, these heat up and cool off more quickly than water does, affecting where the boundaries are between the cells in rather complicated ways. The patterns seen in Figure 4.5, for example, are a bit more complicated than the patterns predicted by the

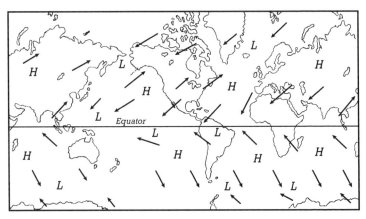

Figure 4.5 Average wind patterns observed on the earth. The winds just above the equator are known as the "NE Trade Winds," those just south of the equator as the "SE Trade Winds." Just above and below the trade winds in both the northern and southern hemispheres are seen the "Prevailing Westerlies." Finally, just above and below the westerlies, in each hemisphere, are seen the "Polar Easterlies". All of these wind patterns are basically explained by the three-cell model of atmospheric circulation. The high-pressure regions (H) and low-pressure regions (L) shown are typical; for example the high pressure region in the North Atlantic is known as the "Bermuda High" and the high-pressure region in the South Atlantic is known simply as the "South Atlantic High." (Adapted *from Invitation to Oceanography*, by P. Pinet.)

three-cell model of Figure 4.4, although the general patterns agree quite well.

Note that the trade winds include the northeasterly winds seen just above the equator and the southeasterly winds seen just below the equator. These are the surface-level winds in the Hadley cell flowing south, but being deflected to the west by the Coriolis force. The northeast trade winds were first used by Columbus to travel from Europe to America, then by the whalers of the nineteenth century, and are still relied upon today by sailors making transits across the Atlantic and Pacific oceans.

Above the easterly trade winds in each hemisphere are seen the previously mentioned westerlies. These include the well-known prevailing westerlies that bring most of the weather across the continental United States. As stated earlier, these are the surface-level winds in the middle cell of each hemisphere, this time being deflected to the east as they try to move northward.

Near the poles are then seen prevailing easterlies, southward-moving winds of the top cell that are deflected to the west by the Coriolis force. At the junction between the northeast and southeast trade winds near the equator, there are the doldrums, the region of general low pressure without much wind, most of the time.

One interesting result of these winds is that they cause currents in the ocean as they blow along the surface of the water for extended periods of time. In fact, if you look at a map of the known ocean currents, it reflects the general wind patterns of Figure 4.5 amazingly well. These currents are shown in Figure 4.6. The ocean currents cannot be exactly like the wind currents primarily because the water currents cannot proceed across the land masses as the wind currents can. But they are still quite close.

For example, there is a strong northern equatorial current moving from Africa to the Caribbean that is caused by the prevailing northeast trade winds discussed above. There is also a strong current in the North Atlantic proceeding from around New England to the British Isles that is caused by the prevailing westerlies.

Because the water flows west in the southern part of the North Atlantic and east in the northern part, there must be a flow northward along the western edge of the Atlantic and southward along the eastern edge. The northward flow along the western edge is, of course, the well-known Gulf Stream. This flow also happens to bring up heated water from the region of the Caribbean and the Gulf of Mexico and carries it all the way across the Atlantic, greatly affecting the climate of Northern Europe. Similar loops are seen in other parts of the world, where a loop is created by the prevailing east-west winds discussed above and closed by north or south flowing currents along the continental land masses.

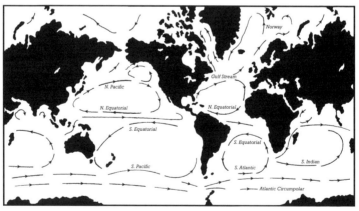

Figure 4.6 The major ocean currents of the world. Note how these follow the global wind patterns rather closely, but are cut off by the land masses and form loops.

While we are discussing winds and water currents, let us say a little about how the wind blowing over the surface of the water produces waves. On a perfectly calm sea, the wind is not able to move the water very well at all. But if the wind continues for a while, especially from one direction, the top of the water will begin to flow, just from the interaction of the moving air molecules with the water molecules on the surface of the water. As the water begins to move, it will make ripples and small eddies.

The initial ripples actually do not move directly in the direction of the wind, but off on both sides at an angle of about 75 degrees. Then, as the ripples increase in size, the wind gets a better "grip" on the water and begins to make waves. As the wind increases to about 5 knots, the moving wave fronts begin to move more in the direction of the wind, and the wind becomes turbulent just above the surface of the water so that the wind interaction with the forming waves becomes more efficient. In fact, as the wind increases and the waves become larger, the energy imparted to the water by the wind increases approximately with the fourth power of the wind. Furthermore, as the waves get bigger, they become more rounded and have longer wavelengths until they reach a point where they will travel almost as fast as the wind.

As we discussed in Chapter 1, water waves are "dispersive," i.e., they move at different speeds for different wavelengths, so longer wavelengths travel faster. Because the wind is able to impart more energy to waves as they increase in size, they will often start to grow rapidly in size as the wind increases. Of course, gravity is always trying to pull waves down, and this effect increases with the size of the waves; so there will be a certain size produced by a certain wind speed, assuming it stays constant and from one direction. Given the right conditions, waves can grow to be quite large. For example, a 60-knot wind lasting for 10 hours makes waves about 45 feet high!

4.3 Tides

The tides are primarily caused by the moon, as most people are aware. Most sailors also know that there are two high tides and two low tides each day. But beyond that, there are a number of common misconceptions regarding tides and their behavior. For example, most people believe that the tidal bulge in the ocean must follow along underneath the moon as the earth turns, so that tides all move across the oceans east to west. This, however, is not true, and in many places the tides actually move west to east. Also, there is relatively little tide near the equator, and none at all in the middle areas of some oceans. These facts surprise most people. Let us see how the tides are formed and how we can understand how the tide moves using simple physics.

The tides are due primarily to the force of gravity that the moon exerts on the earth, and in particular on the oceans of the earth. The force of gravity depends on the distance between the two objects involved. Specifically, it decreases as the square of the distance between the two objects. Gravity also depends linearly on the product of the masses of the two objects. All of this is indicated in Newton's well-known mathematical expression for the gravitational force,

$$F = \frac{GmM}{r^2} \qquad\qquad 4.1$$

Because the force of gravity decreases with distance, it is greater on the water on the side of the earth closer to the moon than on the earth itself, and also greater on the earth than on the water on the far side of the earth away from the moon. These differences cause the water to be pulled away from the earth on the side toward the moon and to pull the earth away from the water on the far side. More specifically, this occurs because there is a disparity between the gravitational force exerted at various points on the earth and the centripetal force needed for circular motion, i.e., the force directed toward the center of revolution (which for the earth-moon system is also the gravitational force).

It is important to note here that in the earth-moon system the moon doesn't just revolve around the earth, but the entire system revolves around a center of mass that is displaced from the center of the earth. It is also important to note that at the center of the earth, the gravitational force from the moon is just equal to the centripetal force required to keep the earth in its circular orbit about the center of mass.

Now, as indicated in equation 4.1, the gravitational force decreases with distance. But the centripetal force required to keep an object moving in a circular path *increases* with distance. Therefore, on the side of the earth that is near to the moon, the gravitational force is stronger than required, and the earth's water, i.e., the ocean, is stretched toward the moon. On the far side, the gravitational force is weaker than required, and the water bulges outward. The net effect is that the water bulges outward from the earth on two sides and there are two high tides per day. The effect is shown diagrammatically in Figure 4.7.

The sun also has this effect on the oceans of the earth, but with a magnitude of less than half of that of the moon. This is because, although the sun has a mass about 80,000 times greater than the moon, it is also about 400 times as far away from the earth. Still, the effect of the sun is significant, and there are larger tides when the sun and moon are aligned, either both on the same side of the earth or directly opposite each other, than when they are at perpendicular directions from the earth. The larger tides are referred to as "spring" tides, and the smaller tides are called "neap" tides.

That there are two high tides and two low tides each day is well known by most sailors. The times of high and low tides at any place on earth are well known from experience. In fact, by observing tides for a few years, it is possible to prepare tide tables for

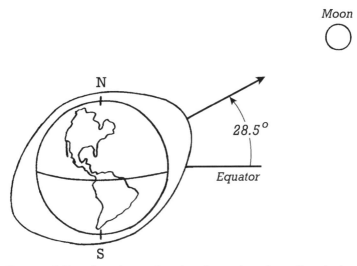

Figure 4.7 A schematic drawing showing the bulge (exaggerated) of the ocean water of the earth due to the gravitational pull of the moon.

the future at that location that, on average, are very accurate, although you still have to say "on average" because the exact time of high and low tides at any point depends on the weather near that place.

High- and low-pressure systems, and especially storm surges, for example, can change the exact time of the tides at any one place from the average time expected. Furthermore, even if we ignore the weather effect and concern ourselves only with the average time of the tides, it is still a somewhat complicated business to understand *exactly* when the tides occur at a particular location thanks to various forces, terrestrial and otherwise.

For example, as we noted earlier there is practically no tide in the ocean near the equator. This is because the plane of the orbit of the moon is tipped at an angle of 28.5 degrees with respect to the plane of the equator of the earth as shown diagrammatically in Figure 4.7. In other words, the plane of the orbit of the moon is closer to the plane of the earth's orbit around the sun, which is tipped at an angle of 23 degrees with respect to the equator. The maximum pull on the ocean water of the earth is along this line at an angle of 28.5 degrees with respect to the equator, as shown. The ocean water near the equator is distorted by the pull of the moon, but this pull is close to the average distortion caused by the moon as shown in Figure 4.7 and remains approximately constant in amount as the earth rotates. The result is that there is relatively little tide near the equator, and this is what is observed. The maximum tides are experienced, as shown, in the middle latitudes, closer to the direction of the moon from the earth.

Next, the speed at which the tide wave moves in the ocean is determined by the *depth* of the ocean. Specifically, for a surface water wave, if the depth is less than about two times the wavelength of the wave, the speed is given by the expression for a "shallow" wave, which can be obtained in a manner similar to the derivation for the speed of deep-water waves presented in Chapter 1. As with other mathematical derivations presented, you can skip the actual derivation in the box below without losing any of the understanding of the explanations that follow. We will, however, use the result of this derivation below.

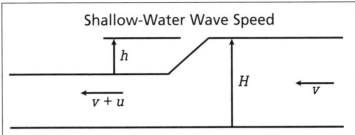

Figure 4.8 A cross sectional view of a surface wave in shallow water.

In Figure 4.8 we consider a shallow surface wave moving toward the left. The "step up" corresponding to the wave is shown as a linear step, i.e., a straight line, but it really doesn't matter what the shape is. Let us consider what is happening as the wave moves over the bottom. The important thing to recognize is that since the water is not accumulating anywhere along its path, the total amount of water coming in at any point must equal the total amount going out. Hence the water must be moving faster in the shallower region to the left than in the deeper region on the right, in order to conserve the flow of water, and this is observed to be true. If we say the speed on the right is v, then on the left side it must be $v + u$. To conserve the amount of water, the product of the velocity times the height at any given point must be constant. Hence, we must have

$$H v = (H - h) (v + u)$$

$$= H v + H u - h v - h u,$$

yielding

$$u (H - h) = h v.$$

Now, if h is small compared to H,

$$u = h\,v\,/\,(\,H - h\,) \approx h\,v\,/\,H. \quad 4.2$$

The kinetic energy of a particle of water on the right is $\frac{1}{2}\,m\,v^2$, and on the left is $\frac{1}{2}\,m\,(v+u)^2$. The difference in the kinetic energies must come from the change in the gravitational potential energy of the particle, which is calculated as $m\,g\,h$; so we must have

$$\tfrac{1}{2}\,m\,(v+u)^2 - \tfrac{1}{2}\,m\,v^2 = m\,g\,h, \text{ or}$$

$$v^2 + 2\,u\,v + u^2 - v^2 = 2\,g\,h, \text{ or}$$

$$2\,u\,v + u^2 = 2\,g\,h.$$

From equation 4.2 we see that since h is taken to be small, $u \ll v$ so that the squared term above can be neglected, and we have

$$u\,v = g\,h.$$

Using 4.2 now for u, we obtain

$$h\,v^2\,/\,H = g\,h,$$

or, solving for v,

$$v = \sqrt{gH}. \quad 4.3$$

The result given by equation 4.3 can be obtained also by solving the appropriate general wave equation for a surface wave and taking the limit for the wavelength longer than the depth. Unfortunately, this general equation is a second-order differential equation and is beyond the level of math we are assuming here. The important point is that you will get the solution indicated above by equation 4.3 for shallow waves, and this solution will not have to assume that h is small compared to H, i.e., that the height of the wave is small compared to the depth. For the tide, the wavelength is one-half the distance around the earth (since high tide comes twice per day), or several thousand miles.

The average depth of the Pacific Ocean, for example, is about 2 km (1.3 miles). Therefore, the depth is much less than the wavelength and equation 4.3 applies. (For this example, h is much smaller than H also, since the height of the tide is usually a few feet or less, compared to the average depth of greater than one mile). Using $H = 2$ km in equation 4.3 yields a speed for the wave of the tide of about 140 m/sec, or about 300 mph.

Since the circumference of the earth is 24,000 miles, the tangential speed at the equator is 1,000 mph and the speed of the wave cannot keep up with the turning of the earth (although there is relatively little tide at the equator anyway). But since the distance around the globe from east to west gets shorter as you move away from the equator, the speed of the wave of the tide begins to be able to keep up with the moon's pull. This means that the system in the mid-latitudes is "semi-resonant," i.e., the pull of the moon is "in sync" with the motion of the tide wave, which can result in larger tides.

Furthermore, in addition to the gravitational attraction from the moon and sun, any motion of the water on the surface of the earth is subject to the Coriolis force, as described above, and will be deflected to the right in the northern hemisphere and to the left in the southern hemisphere. Finally, we note that the oceans of the earth are broken up by the land masses so that the tides are primarily confined to a few large basins. These basins include the North Atlantic, the South Atlantic/Indian Ocean, and the North and South Pacific.

Because of the Coriolis force, a circulation pattern is built up in each basin that circulates counterclockwise in the northern hemisphere and clockwise in the southern hemisphere. These circulation patterns occur twice per day, driven by the spinning of the earth and the gravitational force from the moon. Exactly how fast the circulation pattern moves in a particular region is determined by the depth of the ocean in that region and is affected by undersea mountain ranges, shallow bays, etc.

Finally, each basin has a spot somewhere near its center called an *amphidromic node* around which the circulation pattern revolves and which has essentially no tidal movement. These general circulation patterns are shown for the world's oceans in Figure 4.9. Note how the tides of the North Atlantic are seen to revolve around in a counter-clockwise manner, with an amphidromic point near the center of the North Atlantic. Similar centers of tidal revolution are seen in the South Atlantic/Indian Ocean, and the Pacific Ocean. The tides in the middle of the Atlantic, and also the middle of the Pacific Ocean are indeed known to be only a few inches in height.

It is possible to understand these circulatory patterns of the tides even better by looking at the following sequence of water motion in each basin. Suppose we start with a high tide along the eastern side of a basin in the northern hemisphere created by the gravitational pull of the moon as it rises in the east. This high tide creates a slope in the water

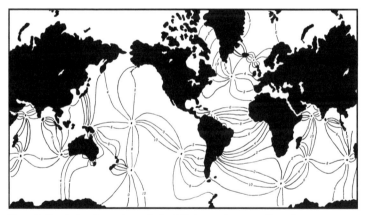

Fig. 4.9 Actual major global tide patterns. The lines are cotidal lines along which the phase of the tide is the same, e.g., all points along a line will experience high tide at the same time. The lines indicate how the tide will move each one hour; making a complete revolution every 12 hours. The co-tidal lines radiate from amphidromic points; these are the centers of revolution of the tides as they proceed CCW in the northern hemisphere and CW in the southern hemisphere. (Adapted from *Invitation to Oceanography*, by P. Pinet.)

angled down toward the west. As the water flows to the west, it is deflected to the right by the Coriolis force, as discussed above for wind motions on the earth. This is a deflection to the north and creates a peaking of the water along the north side of the basin. The peaking in the north creates a flow to the south that is deflected again by the Coriolis force toward the west and creates a new peaking there. This peaking then causes a flow toward the east that is deflected to the south and creates a peaking there. Finally, this peaking creates a flow to the north that is deflected to the east and we have come full circle back to where we started.

This whole process is driven by the gravitational pull of the moon with a 12-hour cycle. The result is a circular flow pattern similar to what you see in a glass of wine when you swirl it gently around, with a "node" in the middle where the surface of the water does not go up or down. Each basin will have a natural period for such a circulatory pattern determined by the speed of the tidal wave in the different parts of that basin. This speed is given by equation 4.3 obtained above.

If the natural period for the water to circulate is close to 12 hours, you will get a resonance excitation of the tides for that basin, because the circulation pattern is in phase with the gravitational pull of the moon. If the natural period for the water to circulate around the basin is very different than 12 hours, you will get a much smaller excitation of the tides. Most of the basins have a natural period that is close to 12 hours, so the tidal excitations are semi-resonant as indicated above. Rotational tidal patterns exist also in some smaller basins that have a natural period close to 12 hours, including the North Sea in Europe and the Gulf of St. Lawrence in Canada.

If, on the other hand, you look at a bay that is relatively long and narrow, the circulatory pattern of tides cannot occur, and what happens instead is a flowing of the tide into the mouth of the bay from the ocean with a 12-hour period. In fact, a closed bay acts like a musical instrument that is closed at one end. Specifically, if the period of the exciting force is close to the time it takes for a wave to go up the bay, be reflected and travel back out the bay, then the process will be resonant, and tides will be greater than normal.

Most bays do not satisfy this requirement and are not resonant. However, a few bays are resonant and therefore experience very dramatic tides. Perhaps the best known example is the Bay of Fundy in Nova Scotia. Its depth is such that the speed of a surface water wave (calculated with equation 4.3 above) is just right to take six hours to go up the bay and six hours to come back out of the Bay, which puts it nicely in phase with the period of the tide at its mouth. When a system is driven at its natural frequency, it is possible to build up very large "standing waves," with the result that tides can be as large as 30 feet in the bay.

Note that you can perform a simple experiment in the bathtub to see this kind of resonance for water waves. While sitting in the tub, start the water sloshing back and forth by using your hands or a small board. When you get the period of oscillation just right, a wave pattern will form along the side of the tub where the crests and troughs are seen to stay at the same place. If you look carefully, you will see that there are an integer number of waves along the side of the tub, usually just one or two full waves. If you continue to push back and forth at the proper rate, very large waves are easily produced that will even start to spill over the sides of the tub. This is resonance, and it occurs because the waves when they reflect off the ends of the tub come back exactly on top of themselves and re-enforce the pattern. If you speed up or slow down the driving frequency, you will see the wave pattern quickly turn into a bunch of "chop" as the reso-nance falls apart with no clearly defined pattern along the sides of the tub as the amplitude of the waves is diminished greatly.

Finally, we note that exactly *when* high tides occur inside bays and estuaries is determined by the time at which the tide from the ocean enters the bay and the speed of a wave up that bay. For exam-ple, the tides in the Chesapeake Bay come from the ocean tide entering the Bay at its mouth, near Nor-folk, Virginia, after which the exact time of the tides inside the bay is determined by the speed with which a surface wave can proceed up the bay. For this reason, the tide at Baltimore lags the tide near Norfolk by about 10 hours, which is just the amount of time expected for a water wave with a velocity given by equation 4.3 above, using the average depth of the Chesapeake Bay of about 20 feet.

In the end, the tides can be fairly well predicted for any point on earth by using observations over a several year period and fitting a mathematical expression to these observations. These tide predictions are available for most places of interest and are what one actually uses for sailing purposes. The above discussion serves to enable us to understand what is really going on with these rather peculiar tides all over the earth.

Further Reading

The following are books that I have found helpful and enjoyed reading in studying some of the physics presented in this book. I recommend any of these to the reader who would like to pursue this subject further or wants more information about some of the related issues, such as sail trim or local weather. Some of these books can be read by anyone; a few require a somewhat higher level of mathematics than assumed in this book.

Fundamentals of Sailing, Cruising and Racing, by Steve Colgate. W.W. Norton, New York, NY, 1978. This is a very good introduction to "how to sail" and does provide some description of the physical principles involved in sailing, including lift. It is an excellent book for the beginning sailor, but does not really attempt to present the physics of sailing in any detail.

Modern Cruising Under Sail, by Don Dodds. The Lyons Press, New York, NY, 1998. This is a somewhat eclectic collection of material of relevance to a sailor interested primarily in cruising. The presentation does include some discussion of the basic physical principles involved in sailing, including for sails and keels. It is a fun read and contains much practical information for the interested cruising sailor.

The Symmetry of Sailing, by Ross Garrett. Sheridan House, Dobbs Ferry, NY, and Adlard Coles Nautical, London 1987. This book is an excellent book describing the physics of sailing in considerable depth. It is a fairly mathematical book, based on a course the author has taught in New Zealand. It covers much of the material presented here in more detail, and covers some topics not discussed here much at all. It is somewhat dated, being written before the present trend toward taller sails and deeper keels. It does not present some of the simple derivations provided in this text, such as for hull speed and Bernoulli's Principle, but it does cover the aerodynamics of sails in depth. It also discusses resistive forces in great detail, although it is a lot of work for the average sailor to extract the basic physical principles of sailing from this work. It does not discuss the physics of tides and currents at all. I recommend this book highly to the person seriously interested in the physics of sailing and willing to work a bit to see some of it done in depth.

Yacht Design Explained, by Steve Killing and Douglas Hunter. W.W. Norton, New York, 1998. This is a nice book with lots of good pictures and charts that describe the basic principles of sailing. The book also discusses some of the history of the development of sailboat design. The discussion is mainly descriptive and does not really attempt to explain "why" the physical principles are true. The book often goes off into various asides that have only limited connection to the basic physics involved, such as the evolution of handicapping formulae or the history of America's Cup designs. It also talks about tank testing and computer modeling. Altogether though, it is a very interesting book.

Principles of Yacht Design, by Lars Larsson and Rolf Eliasson. International Marine, Camden, Maine, 1994. This is another book with lots of pictures and charts, and also lots of equations. The equations are generally quite complex and do not always help the interested sailor to understand what is really going on. Many of the curves and figures are excellent. The discussion tends to be quite technical, with some mathematical complexity. It does provide a good reference book for the serious student of the engineering of sailing, although it will not really allow you to go out and start to design sailboats.

Sailing Theory and Practice, by C.A. Marchaj. Dodd, Mead and Co., New York, 1964 and *Aero-Hydrodynamics of Sailing*, by C. A. Marchaj. International Marine Publishing, Camden, Maine, 1988. These two are classic books on the science of sailing with many diagrams, drawings, charts and tables. The first is a shorter version of the second. These books take an "engineering" approach and simply present many equations without any attempt to derive or justify them from physical principles. They are tomes, especially the second, and are, perhaps, too much for most sailors to try to absorb. They are, however, good reference books for the very serious student of sailing theory. The design descriptions presented are now somewhat dated, these being published before the advent of the deep keels and the tall elliptically shaped sails so prevalent today.

Foundations of Aerodynamics: Bases of Aerodynamic Design, by A.M. Kuethe and C.-Y. Chow, Wiley and Sons, New York, 4th edition, 1985. This is a good textbook on the principles of wing design for the reader interested in pursuing this subject in more depth. The treatment is "engineering" in nature and uses calculus and differential equations.

The New Book of SAIL Trim, edited by Ken Textor, and *The Best of SAIL Trim*, edited by Charles Mason. Sheridan House,

Dobbs Ferry, NY, 2000. These two books, anthologies of authoritative articles from SAIL magazine, include ideas and practices from leading sailors, sailmakers, and designers concerned with all aspect of the sport, from cruising to racing and dinghies to keelboats.

The Science of Flight, by W. N. Hubin. Iowa State University Press, 1995. This is an excellent introduction to the science of flying written for the serious student at the undergraduate level. It includes lots of figures and charts, and lots of very good discussions of the basic principles involved.

Invitation to Oceanography, by Paul R. Pinet. Jones and Bartlett Publishers, Boston, 1998. This is a textbook, but it is an excellent introduction to oceanography, including very good discussions of global weather, ocean currents and tides.

The Sailor's Weather Guide, Second Edition, by Jeff Markell. Sheridan House, Dobbs Ferry, NY 2002. This is a good discussion of weather, especially local weather, from a sailing viewpoint. It provides many helpful discussions of how to use weather wisely while sailing and what to look for in approaching weather.

How to Trim Sails, by Peter Schweer. Sheridan House, Dobbs Ferry, NY 1991. A very good exposition of how to trim sails for different points of sail, different wind conditions, etc. It is a good read and a good book to come back to after trying different sail trims and wanting to know how to continue to improve.

Bores, Breakers, Waves and Wakes, by R. A. R. Tricker. American Elsevier Publishing, New York, 1964. This is a wonderful little book that describes various phenomena having to do with water waves. Although it is older and out of print, it is still available in many libraries. It gives very nice descriptions of tidal bores and wave formation, in a variety of situations.

Sailing Terms

Abeam Perpendicular to the long axis or side of the boat.

Backstay A cable from the stern to the top of the mast to help hold the mast up.

Boom A horizontal beam at the bottom (foot) of the mainsail.

Bow The front end of the boat.

Catamaran A twin-hulled boat.

Close-Hauled Sailing into the direction of the wind as much as possible.

Cockpit The open area on the deck of the boat where the tiller or wheel is located.

Foot The bottom edge of a sail.

Forestay A cable from the bow to the top of the mast. It helps to hold the mast up and the front sail is usually attached to it.

Furl To roll up a sail.

Genoa A front sail attached to the forestay and that extends back past the mast. It is, in some sense, an oversized jib. Such sails are usual on sloops.

Halyard A rope over a pulley at the top of the mast used to raise and lower sails.

Heeling Tipping of the boat away from vertical; usually due to the action of the wind from abeam.

Hull The main body of the boat.

Jib The front sail on a sloop. It is attached to the forestay cable and fills the area between the forestay and the mast.

Jibe To change course from proceeding somewhat off downwind on one side of the wind to somewhat off downwind on the other side of the wind.

Keel A vertical fin attached to the bottom of the keel used to prevent sideslipping and to help reduce heeling.

Leeward Downwind (pronounced "lu-ward").

Line A rope.

Leech The back edge of a sail.

Luff The leading edge of a sail.

Luffing Flopping of the sail due to not having the wind flowing smoothly along it.

Mainsail A large sail located just behind the mast.

Mainsheet A line used to position (trim) the back end of the mainsail.

Port The left side of the boat as viewed from the back of the boat looking forwards.

Pointing Up Sailing more nearly into the direction of the wind.

Reaching A direction (point) of sail with the wind coming mostly perpendicular to the long axis of the boat.

Reef A shortening of the sail, usually at the bottom, in order to reduce the amount of sail area. This is normally done in high wind situations.

Rudder A steering fin located underneath and at the back of the hull.

Running Sailing downwind (or nearly so).

Sheet A line used to locate the bottom and/or back edge of a sail.

Shrouds Cables used to support the mast attached to the mast and to points on the deck along the side of the mast. Some of these may proceed to the top of the mast by passing over the ends of spreader arms located part-way up the mast.

Spinnaker A large, full, triangular-shaped sail used as a front sail primarily for downwind sailing on light-air days.

Spreader Horizontal arms located partway up the mast over which a shroud may pass in order to better strengthen the top section of the mast.

Stanchion A vertical post located near the edge of the deck. Usually wires are strung between stanchions located around the edge of the deck for safety in moving about on the deck.

Starboard The right side of the boat as viewed from the back of the boat looking forward.

Stern The rear end of the boat.

Swing Keel A retractable fin attached to the bottom of the hull. It usually pulls up by use of cables and pulleys.

Tack To change direction from sailing upwind on one side of the wind direction to upwind on the other side of the wind direction. This maneuver requires passing the bow of the boat through the direction straight into the wind.

Tiller A lever attached to the shaft of the rudder used by the helmsperson for steering the boat.

Transom The flat surface at the stern of the hull of the boat.

Trim To adjust the orientation and shape of the sails.

Trimaran A three-hulled boat.

Windward Upwind.

Wing Keel A keel with horizontal fins attached at the bottom to help reduce induced drag (vorticies) and to increase righting moment.

Index

Index

Index